KALE SOUP

My Journey from Music to Macrobiotics

BY

CAROL LOURO

NOTE TO READER:
The information in this book is purely anecdotal, and is in no way intended to be a substitute for medical advice, diagnosis, or treatment. Those with health problems are advised to seek the guidance of a qualified medical practitioner in addition to a qualified macrobiotic counselor before implementing any dietary approaches presented in this book. If you have reason to believe that you have a serious illness, it is essential to seek appropriate medical, nutritional, or psychological advice promptly. No book should be used as a replacement for qualified treatment.

DEDICATION

This book is dedicated to my loving parents whose upbringing opened my mind and heart to recognize the importance of Michio and Aveline's teachings to follow our dream to one peaceful world.

And to my husband, Joe, who encouraged me to pursue my dream of macrobiotics.

ACKNOWLEDGEMENTS

Thank-you to everyone who encouraged and supported me in the writing of this book.

Special thanks to my dear friend, Christin Ritz, who I met through macro-biotics when she started attending my classes. She would often stay after class to chat with me over tea, and we formed a friendship. She ended up moving to Oregon, but the connection we have is strong, and we always stayed in contact. Over the years we talked on and off about the book. When she came back to live in Massachusetts my life had changed—I had lost my husband of 50 years and I needed a purpose. She encouraged me to start up with writing again. This book may not have happened without her help. In addition to all the typing and technical aspects, she transcribed many of my stories, helped me to edit them and organize them into chapters, and guided me along to the end. I'm very grateful. Thank-you, Christin, not only for your help, but for your friendship and gentle soul.

TABLE OF CONTENTS

Preface, by Tom Monte ix
Letters of Introduction xi

Part 1: My Story 1
Chapter 1   This is my Beginning 3
Chapter 2   Our Meeting with Michio and Aveline Kushi 6
Chapter 3   The New Bedford East West Center 10
Chapter 4   My Family and their Journey 15
Chapter 5   Michio and Aveline 18
             Food for Thought on Fourth of July Weekend,
             by Ken Hartnett 22
Chapter 6   The Impact of Food 25
Chapter 7   My Life Transformation: Thank You Papa,
             by Lino Stanchich 31
Chapter 8   A Healing Journey, by Phil Carney 36
Chapter 9   What is Macrobiotics? by John David Mann 44
Chapter 10   Self-Reflection 46
Photos 50

Part 2: The Recipes 59
Grains 62
Soup 67
Beans 75
Vegetables 82
Tempeh, Tofu, and Seitan 87
Sea Vegetables 91
Pickles 95
Special Drinks 98
Desserts 102
Recommended Reading 109

Preface

By Tom Monte

> He who exalts himself will be humbled, and he who humbles himself will be exalted.
>
> —Matthew, 23:12

If anyone embodies this universal truth, it is Carol Louro. She is the humble sage whose simple words and self-effacing manner unexpectedly surprise you with wisdom, power, and light. She gently brings your awareness to small moments and to simple foods that are suddenly illuminated with healing power and love. Like a great cook who chooses to remain unrecognized, Carol Louro sets a humble table and then presents a life-changing meal.

This book is that simple table and that transformational feast.

I have known Carol Louro for more than two decades, and she still has the power to surprise me with a sudden insight or some deep knowledge of healing. You will find examples of this same wonderful characteristic throughout this book.

In these pages, Carol celebrates the great teachers she has worked with, most especially the two greatest of all, Michio and Aveline Kushi. And no doubt, these people deserve her praise for all their great work. But what Carol avoids mentioning is that she has been associated with some of the most remarkable recovery stories in the history of macrobiotics. Numerous people who learned macrobiotic cooking and were guided by Carol—as well as by the Kushis, Steve Gagne, Ed and Wendy Esko, and Marc Van Cauwenberghe—recovered from advanced and life threatening diseases, in many cases defying medical explanation.

It is fair to say that none of these people would have gotten better without Carol's cooking and instruction.

Carol knows firsthand the healing power of the macrobiotic way of life. As she describes here in her book, her father healed his own tubercular kidney disease with macrobiotics, which is how Carol came to know about the diet and philosophy, and about Michio and Aveline Kushi. That experience turned out to be a very good thing, because Carol would later use macrobiotics to cure her own life-threatening cancer.

With so much success helping herself and others get well, you might expect Carol to be a bit strict and doctrinaire. But quite the contrary is true.

"This book is about my journey toward the macrobiotic lifestyle," Carol writes in her very first sentence, informing us that that lifestyle is an ideal to which one strives. We are human, she is saying, and therefore ever-evolving—not toward some conceptual image of perfection, but toward a greater wholeness. Carol's humanity is what shines forth in these pages, and in the process reveals what is most beautiful about being human.

Thus, when Carol gives us little anecdotes about her own diet, she avoids any implied perfection, and instead reveals her appreciation for muffins, barley malt, and too much miso soup.

This is more than a cookbook, just as Carol Louro is more than a macrobiotic chef. In these pages, Carol provides the recipes and instructions needed to restore your health and happiness. And all of it is presented with Carol Louro's very special ingredients—humility, humor, wisdom, and love.

When you step into Carol's cooking class you will meet people from all walks of life. While macrobiotics sometimes falls under a new age category of alternative health, hers was not a class of twig-like yogis. There are all types of folks in the kitchen: some sick, some in good health, people who had been attending weekly for decades, others hearing about macrobiotics for the very first time, people recovering from drug and alcohol problems, curious college students interested in alternative ways of life, immigrants speaking broken English; and you might even run into your mailman, grocery store clerk, doctor or priest while you're there. At Carol's class you'll see a group of people who don't seem to have anything in common with each other, until you see them all intently listening to Carol explain why she is cooking the way she is, and then of course the camaraderie when they start eating and sharing the food that will give them all the same great energy that Carol has created on the stovetop.

Why does Carol attract such a diverse crowd? For so many years she's treated everyone as a friend, sincerely wants to help each person with their ailment, is never judgmental, always kind, and cooks the most delicious food. With a kind heart and welcoming demeanor, she exemplifies the fact that macrobiotics is for *everybody*.

I have seen many people begin on their path to wellness and recovery in Carol's kitchen, where with her husband and best friend she faithfully held a cooking class every Wednesday night for over 30 years. Guided by her macrobiotic cooking expertise and encouragement, people would transform their illnesses to restored health. Carol started her macrobiotic journey in the 1970s, under the tutelage of Michio and Aveline Kushi, Ed Esko, Marc Van Cauwenberghe, Steve Gagné, Wendy Esko, and Tom Monte, some of the best teachers and counselors of macrobiotics in the world. But many years of study and practice alone is not enough to be as masterful a teacher and cook as Carol is. It also takes a pure heart and a generous soul. Carol's nature shows a love for all people, and that energy becomes tangible when you taste her meals.

Others recognized these qualities in Carol too, and I was pleased to hear she was recognized with the honor of the Aveline Kushi Award, which is given out annually to individuals dedicated to macrobiotics. I am blessed to know Carol Louro, and doubly blessed to count her as a friend. With what I now know about how food affects our bodies and minds, I can say I would be a different person had I not met Carol when I did, and mean that literally! It is my hope that this book, filled with her stories and recipes, will spread her knowledge and love to you, and bring peace and wellness to your life. From one grain, ten thousand grains.

Christin Ritz

Carol is one of the most unique and caring individuals I have ever known. I first met her at a neighborhood New Year's Eve party in 1980. I commented on the huge salad sitting in the middle of the buffet table and was directed to Carol because it was for her. I was happy I asked because Carol told me her story and over the years we became personal and professional friends. As time went on I saw that Carol put her own fears, nervousness, and reluctance to do things aside to get the message about macrobiotics out. She taught classes, gave lectures, and was on television. She appeared on many different radio shows including mine where we talked about the energetics of food. She is one of those rare individuals who make the world a better place. She's an extraordinary woman and I treasure our friendship.

Meryl Novek

I have known Carol for more than 50 years. None of that time has been boring, and if you know Carol, you know what I mean.

Carol and I were acquaintances so long ago. But that changed when Carol was diagnosed with cancer. I found out that she was taking a bus to Boston for some kind of special cooking class. I thought it would be a kind gesture to offer to drive her to Boston instead of her going alone... besides, it was only once a week. Little did I know, my life would never be the same.

Looking back I don't even know how long it took us to complete Levels One and Two...of course Carol went further until she completed her teaching requirements. Carol has an insatiable appetite for knowledge.

One of the special moments at the very beginning of all this, was when Edward Esko very excitedly told us what a great idea it would be to start macrobiotic cooking classes in New Bedford! Well you would have to be there. Carol was so excited, she couldn't contain herself and I couldn't speak because my jaw had dropped! Meanwhile Ed and Carol were planning food menus and planning lectures and possible venues. You get the picture. I made a weak argument against all of it, but I didn't stand a chance. Besides, I rarely have a chance to win an argument with Carol.

The long and short of it is it's the best thing that ever happened to me.

These 50 plus years we have shared the happiest times and some of the saddest times TOGETHER.

She is the sister I never had.

And the person I can count on, ALWAYS!

Lorraine DeCosta

I am one of five children born through Michio and Aveline Tomoko Kushi. I was born in New York City in 1954. As a child, I had no idea or any other life to compare the circumstances in which I grew up as anything unusual. It has taken a lifetime to really appreciate the rather unique circumstances I was raised in.

Some of the not so surprising benefits has been the fact that my life has been virtually sickness free. The last stomach ache I had was in August 1972, never experienced a headache, and have never taken medications of any kind. Humorously, as I write this, I am just getting over a cold, the first one I've had in over 5 years.

Another benefit that I see linked to the way in which I was raised, is a understanding and feeling of connection with the universe in a way that seems to be missing with many of us in our modern age. There is always a sense of trust and knowing that all things are fundamentally okay, and regardless of what is arising, a trust and knowing that it has its place in the grand scheme of the universe.

What I consider has been the greatest benefit in the way I was raised, is having grown up with a literal international family. There are thousands of people from all over the world that I've had the privilege to get to know. From a young age, I felt a real connection with people from all over the globe. For a youngster with wanderlust, this has been a real benefit that I did not recognize till I was much older. The ability to travel anywhere in the world and stay with friends has been quite magical. I remain friends with many of the people who have passed through the doors of our home.

Carol Louro and her family are friends that have passed through our home that I've happily remained in contact with over the years. Without people like Carol, the work of my parents could never have happened. It is through listening to her story and others like hers that I began appreciating the unusual circumstances in which I was raised. Her father and family have had an impact in our life as well. From her father, I was gifted my first guitar and flute, over 40 years ago. I moved away from music during the more serious period of my life when I was pursuing an illusory idea of success. Happily, I returned to my love of wheels, and at the same time, picked up the guitar again.

Living the life I enjoy, I've gained incredible insights into the nature of reality and the true purpose of being human. When the desire to share these insights arose, the friendship I maintained with Carol and her family was right there, supporting me with my endeavors. Carol immediately invited me to New Bedford, and provided an open space where I could share the insights into the true nature of being human. As it was for my parents, it is friendships I enjoy with human beings like Carol that are an integral part of living a worthwhile life. Humanity is in good hands.

Thank you Carol and to your beautiful family.
Norio Kushi

By Sara Soares

PART 1
My Story

CHAPTER 1

THIS IS MY BEGINNING

This book is about my journey toward the macrobiotic lifestyle, as well as some of my favorite recipes and helpful tips on how to prepare macrobiotic meals.

My father, Lionel, a musician, was always investigating different paths to health. He had a peaceful, childlike demeanor and was open-minded to different philosophies. His positive attitude towards people and life had a strong impact on me very early on. From my infancy until first grade my mother, Sara, brother, Carl, and I traveled with my father and the big bands all over the United States. Once we settled down and I started school, from first through fifth grade we would travel from May until September with the big bands all through New York and Canada. Now, when I look back at the memories I realize that was the beginning of my journey to macrobiotics. I will explain how and why.

As a child I spent many hours backstage with performers, but mostly with the Rockettes. One day I asked Lena, the seamstress, why she had numbers on her arm, "Did you mother let you get tattoos?" I saw the sadness in her face at my young age and she explained that she was in a camp and wasn't given much food and very cold water. Her stomach would hurt so badly for hours and hours.

Then she hugged me so tight and told me, "I got out and God brought you to me so I wouldn't have to be backstage alone." I will never forget that and believe that if we have our hearts and minds open, people come into our lives for special reasons. I think that way because of Lena. Now, looking back on my life I see that my friendship with Lena backstage is what influenced my interest in world peace and the macrobiotic lifestyle.

When we would leave for the state fairs just a few weeks before the summer, Carl would miss his friend Gilly, and I would miss my friend Michele, and of course our dog, Goldie. My Uncle Lou would take good care of her. We had mixed emotions—excited about traveling with the band but also missing our friends. Good thing we had each other. Carl and I would sit in the back of my parents' pickup truck pulling the trailer that we would live in for the summer. Well, to our surprise when we arrived at our first destination a young boy our age approached us with a big, warm smile saying he was part of the traveling band. He told us he would be performing, and asked if he could he hang out with us when he was done.

"YES!" we said, and became very close with him for years. His name was Ralph Heid. Ralph was a world renowned xylophone player. When he wasn't performing we would walk all over the fairgrounds hanging out together. Then when night came and Ralph was done we would lie down in the middle of the fairground racetrack and watch the stars and listen to the band. My favorite song was "Moonlight Serenade," maybe because my father was playing the clarinet solo. We lived in the middle of the racetrack, so we could stay out until the show was over.

This is irrelevant but I think this story should be told. The second year we traveled with the band we had just arrived at the racetrack and my brother and I were walking around. Harpo Marx saw us and said to me, "Carol, Ralph is looking for you. He's here already." I was shocked, I didn't know Harpo could talk! He walked off laughing. Harpo was an amazing musician and very warm and friendly with us. He was humble and kind.

A couple of years later Ralph went on the Mickey Mouse TV show. He and his parents stayed with us for a few weeks and he performed at my school, Joseph DeMello Elementary in Dartmouth, MA. But again to my surprise when we were having breakfast Mr. Heid had his sleeves rolled up and again, numbers on his arm. He told us that yes, he was in a camp! He went to Switzerland when he got out. We have pictures of Mr. and Mrs. Heid in my parents' living room and they were *always* smiling. They were so kind and gentle. I cannot imagine what they endured.

By Carl Lionel Soares

CHAPTER 2

OUR MEETING WITH MICHIO AND AVELINE KUSHI

Life moves on. My father ended up with a tubercular kidney and the doctors recommended he have it removed. He heard about a healer from Japan named Michio Kushi. He went to his house in Boston for a consultation, thinking that by going on the macrobiotic diet he would recover more quickly from his surgery. Well, he never had his kidney removed and lived until ninety-one years old in a good state of health and mind. He and my mother were going to Arlington Street Church in Boston to study with Michio and his wife, Aveline. I was very intrigued with the manuscripts they would bring home from Michio's lectures, the questions from the students, and the answers from Michio. I read about his philosophy on world peace and how food has an impact not only on our health but also our emotions and thinking. He taught that the way to world peace starts with each individual person. The goal of the macrobiotic lifestyle is to create a peaceful demeanor within ourselves, and by creating that we radiate love, peace, and harmony towards everyone around us. I read about how Michio was devastated by World War II and committed his life to promoting peace. That brought me back to my relationship with Lena.

One day my father said, "I want you to meet Michio and Aveline." When we were in the car ready to leave my father said, "Hold on!" and ran into the house where his music store was connected and came out with three guitars and a flute.

I asked him, "Why are you bringing instruments to this man?"

He said, "I am not giving Michio enough for all he has done for me, and he has many children."

That made me think.

When we met Michio the first thing he said to me was that I was going to be a macrobiotic teacher, and that I had eaten enough butter for this lifetime and the next. We laughed and he just stared at me smiling. Next, he had my husband lie down on the floor and he walked on his back, which totally shocked us. Then he looked at me, smiled, and said, "Husband eats much meat." He was right, my husband only ate meat and potatoes. He never ate salad, and he owned a meat market! That experience with Michio left us totally confused and we couldn't understand how he could know how we lived when we hadn't told him a thing. That is when we found out about oriental diagnosis. A good book to read more about this is <u>Your Face Never Lies</u> by Michio Kushi.

A few months later I found out I had cancer in stage four. It was 1979 and I was also pregnant at the time. My doctor wanted to wait until the baby was delivered before we decided what route to take. I can remember walking out of the doctor's office in complete shock and fear for the future, not only for myself, but also for what was in store for my husband and children. I called to make an appointment with Michio, but he was out of town. The person on the phone said, "You could see another macrobiotic counselor, and from the sound of your voice you should see someone soon." Hearing his voice I felt like he would be a good support system for me, so I asked him if he was a counselor. He said yes. I had my first meeting with Steve Gagné and many more after that. He gave me dietary recommendations to help improve my condition. Being on a healing diet was not so difficult for me because of my love for my husband and four children, and that I was so afraid to leave them.

Here is a story about how our mind has a big impact on our well-being. I called Steve a few weeks after my consultation and said, "I'm not going to die of cancer." He told me he wished everyone thought like that. "No, you didn't let me finish," I continued, "I'm not going to die of cancer—I'm so scared I'm going to have a heart attack!"

I had been a big fruit eater, and in my first meeting he had permitted me to continue having fruit. After this, he told me not to eat any fruit for a while, to only drink when I was thirsty, and I wouldn't be so fearful.

After this Michio called and told me to see a spiritual friend. I went to speak to a priest and he asked me how I felt when I prayed.

"Not good," I answered.

"But why, Carol?" he asked.

"Because of the Our Father prayer. 'Thy will be done,' If God wants me to die, then I'll die."

He looked down for a long time. I didn't interrupt him. He said, "God only wants good for us. If God takes you, your family will be okay, and if he doesn't then maybe he has a different path for you." He knew I was starting the macrobiotic diet and he suggested I not tell many people about my illness so they wouldn't discourage me. He told me to listen to happy music, which was very interesting because that's exactly what Michio always told us. When I walked out of that room I was never afraid again.

I was very diligent at sticking to my diet and in about a year I had completely recovered from my illness. My doctor, who was very kind to me, was confused that all my symptoms were gone. He told me to please come back every three months for a year to be sure. Since then, my symptoms have never returned.

When Michio came back I made an appointment to have a consultation with him and the first thing he said to me was, "I told you you're going to be a macrobiotic teacher." I started taking some cooking classes at the Kushi Institute in Boston, and was taking the bus and subway there by myself. My friend, Lorraine, felt bad for me traveling alone and started going with me. Then Michio, Aveline, and Edward Esko, a prominent macrobiotic counselor, suggested I take all the macrobiotic levels at the Kushi Institute. The levels are courses that offered a comprehensive training in all aspects of macrobiotics from cooking to diagnosis, and from philosophy to healthcare. I took all three levels and went to a macrobiotic center in Becket, MA to get my certification to teach and lecture on macrobiotics.

I grew up having soup almost every day, mostly kale soup, which is a Portuguese tradition. When I started taking macrobiotic cooking classes I was surprised to see how kale was cooked and treated as a vegetable dish. Previously I had only eaten kale in soup. I didn't realize how healthy kale is for us. I am thankful to my ancestors for all the kale they grew and cooked.

I remember when I was studying, Edward Esko came down with friends. I served them miso soup in large bowls. When they were done I asked, "Would you like another bowl?"

Right away Edward said, "No, Carol, miso soup is very salty! You should serve it in a small bowl." Then he said, "No wonder you're getting so yang. I couldn't figure it out." Well, I'm glad I learned that lesson as soup is one of my favorite dishes.

As part of my certification I was given a topic and one hour to write about it. Then I had to read what I had written to a panel of counselors who would ask me questions. My topic was "What is a Beginner's Mind?" I feel so blessed that this was my topic because I still think about this all the time. We all need to learn to have a beginner's mind and take advantage of it. Life is always bringing us lessons, which is a very good thing. There are always new things coming into our lives and new friends with different outlooks that are interesting and fun. By keeping our minds open we embrace a beginner's mind. When you start a new job, go away to college, a new mother has a baby, et cetera, with this kind of mindset we can travel new paths. Practicing macrobiotics brings us to a beginner's mind, and by having one we open ourselves up to new adventures. Our hearts open and our intuition becomes clear.

CHAPTER 3

THE NEW BEDFORD EAST WEST CENTER

Lorraine and I opened the New Bedford East West Center for Macrobiotics with the help of Edward Esko, Wendy Esko, Marc Van Cauwenberghe, M.D., Evelyne Harboun, and Clyde Motosue in the early 1980s. Starting out I was excited about teaching but also a little apprehensive. Edward asked me, "But Carol, who in New Bedford knows how to make miso soup?"

He's right—I thought, *not many people!*

We gave cooking classes four times a week, hosted monthly lectures with the counselors, and offered shiatsu massages and consultations. I think our cooking classes were popular because in addition to cooking instruction we talked about the philosophy behind macrobiotics and which foods help different problems. We hosted some lectures at UMass Dartmouth to a completely full house. I also taught evening classes at New Bedford High School and the Greater New Bedford Vocational High.

Steve Gagné was a lecturer who attracted many people. He later went on to write The Energetics of Food which is an interesting book. Once he began to tell the story of when I called and told him I would have a heart attack before I died of cancer. As he began he looked at me and started to laugh. Then I looked at Lorraine and she looked back at Steve, and we were all laughing thinking about the story that was about to be told. It lightened everyone's mood. That lightheartedness is the nature of macrobiotics. Again, I'm repeating it, but our way of thinking has a huge impact on our well-being.

The New Bedford, Massachusetts area has a large Portuguese population. With the help of Francisco "Chico" Varatojo, who ran a very successful macrobiotic center in Lisbon, Portugal, Michio arranged for Antonio "Tozé" Areal to stay with us for a year and teach in Portuguese to reach more of the Portuguese speaking community. Ed Esko, Alex Jack, Tozé, and I were invited to speak on local radio stations which helped spread the word, and had many articles written about us as well. To this day many people remember the impact Tozé and the other macrobiotic teachers had on our community.

Marc Van Cauwenberghe, who had been a medical doctor in Belgium before coming to the States, was always writing books and explaining different illnesses and personalities to us. He loved having the radio on playing happy music.

This is a story that I'm happy telling. When Wendy Esko came for the first time to give a cooking class I was apprehensive to serve her my soup. She tasted it and to my surprise said, "This tastes good!" Then another taste and said, "Yes, very good!" I was so happy she thought that! Wendy was one of the most inspiring people I ever worked with. Her insight to what foods people needed was phenomenal.

When she gave classes, Wendy never looked down as she cut the vegetables. We would say, "Wendy! You're going to cut your fingers!"

"No," she would say, "I know where my fingers are. I'm okay." We always had many laughs with Wendy. We had good food and learned so much. She is still a good friend of mine.

Evelyne Harboun is one of those people who brings a calming energy to wherever she is. Her demeanor just makes you feel relaxed, so we always enjoyed peaceful evenings when she would come down to teach, and her meals were incredibly delicious too!

Diane Avoli and Bettina Zumdick were both very interesting teachers. After the Kushi Institute moved out of Boston and went to western Massachusetts I was fortunate to have their support hosting classes in New Bedford when many teachers had left the area. Diane's classes were always lighthearted and fun.

Bettina is an extremely precise person and her classes always end exactly at the time they are scheduled. At one summer conference I was in charge of keeping an eye on the time and making sure the classes moved along. The coordinator reminded me to watch the clock. "Oh you don't have to worry about Bettina," I said, but she was still nervous. Bettina ended the class precisely to the minute of the session. The woman who was coordinating apologized and said she'd never doubt me again!

One night Warren Kramer was teaching a cooking class with us and making his delicious tempura. All the students loved it and were asking for more. Joe, Lorraine, and I kept saying, "Cook, Warren! More tempura! More tempura!" It was such fun—maybe you would have to be there, but it wasn't just the food that was enjoyable that night, but also the moment.

All the counselors were very dedicated and would stay with us three or four days at a time to teach and offer personal guidance. They were all entertaining, easy to be around, and we became very close with all of them. I must say that the macrobiotic community does live the lifestyle. They were always available 24-7 for anyone that needed additional guidance or advice.

A few years before Michio moved the Kushi Institute to Becket, Massachusetts, the Level 3 students would come to New Bedford for dinner lectures, and a teacher named Richard would grade them. After the lectures they would all end up at our house, playing guitars, telling stories, and having lots of fun!

Lorraine and I had many great times together cooking for the dinner lectures we hosted at the center. Everyone has their favorite tastes. The five flavors in macrobiotic cooking are sweet, salty, sour, pungent, and bitter. One night we were making Sweet and Sour Tempeh. Lorraine tasted it and said, "Oh, it needs more vinegar."

After she added the vinegar I tasted it and said, "Now, it needs more barley malt," and added some more.

After going back and forth doing this about three times, we looked at each other. "Wait a minute," Lorraine said, "What flavor are you looking for?"

"Sweet," I said, "What flavor are you looking for?"

"Sour!" she said, and we burst out laughing.

Tempeh, tofu, and seitan are all high protein foods used in macrobiotic cooking. Seitan is traditionally made by washing wheat flour over and over until the bran separates and you are left with the gluten, which is formed into balls and simmered in a dashi broth. It is a very time consuming process to make from scratch, but when I started macrobiotics it wasn't yet available in stores so it was the only way. Luckily my kids were young enough that I could give them five dollars and get them to work all day making seitan for our cooking class! Boy, what was I thinking back then?

All four of my children, Chris, Tracy, Aimee, and John, also became close with the counselors. My older two, Chris and Tracy, would always help out at dinner lectures serving the food and collecting the tickets. Steve would bring them to the coffee shop and they would keep him company while he prepared his speeches, and of course they would get plain donuts. Even being immersed in the world of macrobiotics, they learned not to be judgmental about people's food choices. We learn by example. No matter what they were eating or what foods their friends brought into the house, the counselors never told my children not to eat this or that food. But I must say, when they did get sick we would tell them that it must be from what they had been eating the last few days. This made them realize how different foods can affect their health. My children were curious and were always asking Ed and Marc, "What do you think *this* food does?" The lesson my children learned from macrobiotics that I like most is not to judge people on what they choose to eat, and not to worry about being judged themselves. They very well know the impact that food has on our health and emotions.

We had relationships with some of Michio and Aveline's children too, and they would work with us in New Bedford. Norio Kushi came to New Bedford to talk about the dedication his parents had to helping people and promoting world peace. Phiya Kushi would sometimes drive Michio down for his lectures. Lawrence Kushi, M.D. participated in a group panel on macrobiotics that we hosted at UMass Dartmouth.

After many years of working with us, Marc told me he would be leaving the area. We went out to eat and I asked him, "Who is going to take your place and work with us?"

"Tom Monte," he answered.

"What? But Tom is famous. He doesn't know me! He won't work with me. Would you call him for me, Marc?"

"No. You have to call him yourself," he replied.

I thought to myself, *No, I'm not calling Tom Monte.*

Marc softly smiled and said, "If Tom says no, I will talk to him. But you must call. It's going to be okay."

Something about the way Marc looked at me gave me the confidence to make the call to Tom. When I called, Tom answered on the second ring. I explained who I was, what counselors I was working with, and that I knew the Kushis.

To my surprise, right away he said, "Yes, I'll work with you."

"Don't you need to talk to Michio or Marc about me first?" I asked.

"I don't need to," Tom said, "I can hear your voice." Then with a laugh he added, "And you know Michio and Aveline, who else do you need to know? Let me give you my telephone number."

What's he talking about? I thought, *I've got the number—I just called HIM!*

"I never answer this phone," he continued, "I only answer my office phone, but for some reason, this time I wanted to know who was calling."

I was amazed. I remembered what I learned from Lena, that God brings special people into our lives. I feel blessed because of the SPECIAL people that not only came into my life, but became close friends. Tom went on to work with us for over twenty years.

Opening the center was a very rewarding experience given the support we received from so many friends in the New Bedford area, Michio and Aveline, and all the counselors and cooking teachers. Some teachers only came once or twice but I am so grateful for what they did.

CHAPTER 4

MY FAMILY AND THEIR JOURNEY

This chapter is about how my husband and children adapted to the macrobiotic lifestyle. When I was beginning the macrobiotic diet and trying to improve my illness I was cooking lots of medicinal drinks and dishes. I asked my husband and two older children if Tuesday night we could all eat macrobiotic. To my delight they agreed! Besides my own healing, eating macrobiotic affected the health of my family as well.

Now Chris, my oldest, was always having pain in the front of his legs. His pediatrician suggested we get orthopedic shoes for him and also sent him to an ear, nose, and throat doctor. After x-rays and examining him, the doctor gave me a pamphlet with the rules on how to take care of Chris. I was to wash his bedroom window every day, he was to change clothes in a room other than his bedroom, and I was supposed to make his bed when he was out of the room.

Well, we decided to bring him to see Michio. When Michio entered the room, he looked at Chris and Chris put his head down. Michio then preceded to bend over to see his face. Before we knew it Chris had his face looking down so much that Michio could barely see it. Michio didn't tell Chris to pick his head up. Instead he laid down on the floor and looked up to see Chris' face. Well of course that made Chris laugh and he became comfortable with Michio. He told us that Chris' kidneys were in trouble but the doctors wouldn't find out for five more years. That's what was causing the pain in Chris' legs. Chris followed the diet for weak kidneys very well for a young boy. He was only eleven years old.

When we went back to the pediatrician's office, his doctor was surprised to find he wasn't in the same condition. His legs had stopped hurting and he didn't need surgery. Of course this was the first time the doctor mentioned to me that Chris might have to have his tonsils removed. The doctor said to me, "This has never happened before. I was going to tell you today that Chris needs to have his tonsils taken out, but you did everything I told you to do and now he is better."

I didn't tell the doctor that Chris had changed his diet. When we got to the car Chris said to me, "Mom, you didn't do it, I did!" I always felt guilty I didn't say that to the doctor. To this day Chris doesn't eat any meat or poultry and stays pretty macrobiotic.

My youngest son, John, has always had a very open personality. One day, when he was about 4 years old we were at the beach. I heard him calling to me, "Hey, Mom!"

I looked and saw him standing by the water holding up big handfuls of black seaweed, "Isn't this what we eat at home?" All the people sitting nearby were looking at us strangely, and of course his older siblings were extremely embarrassed! Looking back, my family laughs about that story now.

We lived just up the street from John's school. When he was in seventh grade his friends were hanging out at our house daily. Sometimes I would get pizza for them, John included. They also liked fried chicken. John started eating that way with his friends, and he also started not feeling so well.

I brought him to the doctor and blood tests were taken. The doctor thought it was John's liver and wanted to put him on a special diet for six months. When the doctor left the room to get the diet for John, John said, "Mom! Can you put me on a macrobiotic diet for maybe six weeks? I can't be on a diet for six months. Remember Phil, Mom? He got better fast."

John was talking about a man who had come to some classes and turned his health around with macrobiotics. So I went up to the doctor and told him what John wanted to do. The doctor looked at me, put his pen down and said, "Okay, little Johnny's on. We'll check his blood in six weeks."

Well, John did well with his eating and after he had his bloodwork done, the doctor called and asked to speak with him. He congratulated John on his good results and said, "Wow. You did so well. Good for you John!"

My daughter, Aimee, was helped through macrobiotics too. Aimee had a fibroandenoma and experienced positive results practicing the diet.

Like I said, my husband had been a meat and potato eater. He started changing his diet too, and many years later became macrobiotic. We went to Michio's house in Boston, and when Michio saw Joe he looked surprised. He said, "Who is that standing there?" At first we couldn't understand why Michio would say this because he had known Joe for so many years, but eating well not only impacts your internal health, but also your outward appearance. Using oriental diagnosis, Joe looked very different to Michio. Michio walked over to Joe, shook his hand, and congratulated him for how much he had changed. Joe always treasured that moment.

Chapter 5

Michio and Aveline

When I think about being at Michio's house in the 1970s, I remember there were so many people waiting for hours to see him. Many people would be lying on the floor sleeping. There was a basket where people would leave donations. Aveline was always very kind and would bring tea during the consultations. I remember seeing his children come home from school and go upstairs. Years later Michio's son, Norio, came to our center and explained what it was like in those days with his parents offering so much help and guidance all day, then lecturing at night. Such a big sacrifice from all of them, I understand why my father's heart opened to Michio's children when he gave them the musical instruments. I often remember what Michio told us, that enjoying music everyday provides us a very good therapy. The best is happy music and relaxing music.

Michio and Aveline helped many people during the AIDS crisis in the 1980s. Once, while Aveline was giving a cooking class, a man said, "Thank-you, Aveline. You are the first person to not judge us." The heartfelt need for world peace was so great in the Kushis' hearts and minds.

Many people in our Southeastern Massachusetts community would go to Boston to receive consultations with Michio. Often I would go with them. One day I was sitting on the floor next to Michio, who always sat on the floor. He wrote on the coffee table while his friends who were having the consultations sat on the couch or chair.

He asked me to give Thomas, his assistant, my fax number so he could contact me. I replied, "I don't have a fax number."

He then asked, "Do you have an email address?"

I again replied, "No."

Then he asked, "Do you have a cell phone?"

I was very embarrassed and couldn't look at him. I said, "No."

Then he said, "Great! You simple human like Michio!" Michio always spoke about himself in the third person. We all started laughing!

From then onward we just used the house phone. That was the start of Michio coming to our area to lecture. He also gave consultations when he was here. Michio would come early before the lecture and visit with Joe and me, then return to our house after the lecture ended and visit until 1AM. Yes, Michio was not only inspirational to be around, but a lot of fun to be with.

Another time, a couple was having a consultation with Michio and I was helping with the notes. When Michio began guiding them on desserts he said, "Okay, you can have two to three tablespoons of barley malt a week."

The man said very surprised, "WHAT? I thought you could drink that stuff, Michio!"

At that moment Michio put his pen down and looked straight into my eyes. Of course I didn't say anything. Michio then picked up his pen and started looking at his notes in deep thought. Then he said, "Ah, Carol, so famous for her barley malt!" Michio was always lighthearted and having fun. But yes, I would eat barley malt by the spoonful. I don't anymore, but it took a while.

That story was told at many of my cooking classes. When I would reflect on it people always laughed; I feel the message they got is that yes, we all crave, and at times go over the top, but then you can get back into balance.

Michio never scolded anyone for not following his recommendations. He would gently explain to them the reason why they were binging and not able to stay on the diet. Some of the reasons they were binging would be because they were eating too much baked flour like bread or muffins. They may have been using too much salt in their cooking, or not bringing enough variety into their meals. Michio always ended his consultations with the advice to sing a happy song every day.

This story illustrates Michio's lighthearted sense of humor. I would go to Michio's house with people to support them during their consultation and take notes on his recommendations. One day on our way over we stopped to eat at Open Sesame, a popular macrobiotic restaurant in Boston. After our lunch I ordered squash pie and so did Paul. Well, when Michio started questioning Paul about his diet he said, "Are you eating too much fruit?"

Paul said, "No."

Then Michio asked, "Are you eating too many sweets?"

Paul said no again.

At that point Michio relaxed and said with a smile, "Wow, you living saint!"

Paul relaxed too and said, "Yes, but just today I had squash pie."

So I informed Michio that I ordered squash pie and had told Paul it would be okay for him to have a piece too.

Michio laughed and said to me, "You angel! No, you don't want to be angel. Then you won't be on earth. Instead, you ninja!" At that point we were all relaxed and not concerned about right and wrong.

So Michio explained that Paul was eating way "too narrow," "not enough variety," and the pie was fine to have because it was a macrobiotic dessert made with rice syrup. The consultation was a very insightful one because Michio explained how we need variety—not only different foods, but different cooking methods. We need to be conscious, especially on a healing diet, to not only use different styles of cooking but to use all five flavors every day.

The last time Michio came to New Bedford to lecture was in 2004. As I introduced him I mentioned some of the honors he had received, including the 1994 Award of Excellence from the United Nations Society of Writers, and that the Smithsonian Institution's National Museum of American

History had created a permanent collection of his and Aveline's work in 1999. After the lecture was over Michio was visiting at our home and said to me, "Thank you very much for saying that about Michio, but what's important in Michio's life is that you are Michio's friend."

I feel blessed that when he would come down, Michio would always spend time visiting with us. That was a very heartwarming experience for me. I am so grateful to have not only met Michio and Aveline, but also to have gotten to know their family. What the Kushis have given, not only to me, but also to my family and our community, I can never repay in my lifetime. I am so grateful to have been able to experience my father's altruism and his generosity to others by seeing him share his love of music with Michio and Aveline's children. It was because he was so grateful for what Michio had done for him. This confirms that some the largest gifts in life are the smallest friendships that blossom into the most meaningful and heartfelt friendships.

This article was written by Ken Hartnett who was the editor of the Standard-Times in New Bedford, Massachusetts. He attended our weekly cooking classes and wrote several articles about our center. We were fortunate to have him write this article about Michio Kushi's last lecture in New Bedford.

FOOD FOR THOUGHT ON FOURTH OF JULY WEEKEND

By Ken Hartnett, Editor of The Standard-Times

Here is a prediction I'm daft and dumb enough to make on Fourth of July weekend: The next burning American issue is going to involve the food we eat.

Go ahead and bite into that juicy burger or sausage you just took off the grill, and enjoy the company of your family on this glorious holiday.

But do you ever wonder that for most of us it takes a holiday or a birthday to get the whole family together for food?

That's part of the food issue. It involves not just what we eat but how we eat, and that's critical, because how and what we eat is so central to who we are and how we live as individuals and as a people.

The food question was at the fore a week ago at a small but significant gathering at a downtown church.

More than 100 people who represented a broad cross section of SouthCoast life assembled to hear a three-hour lecture by a vigorous man of 78 named Michio Kushi, making his first New Bedford appearance in almost 10 years.

The basis of Mr. Kushi's teaching is that unless human beings get better physically, mentally, and spiritually, there can be no peace. His approach to life is called macrobiotics.

How and what people eat is

central to his teaching. It's not just the food that is important; it's the way it is prepared and the way it is consumed.

In his belief system, the families who eat together stay together, and more than a casual relationship exists between fast-food-eat-on-the-run American families and the high divorce rate. Not surprisingly, macrobiotics calls for an eating regimen radically different from what the great majority of Americans follows. For one thing, you never eat unless you are sitting down.

Macrobiotic folks eat no meat, no animal products; no beef, no chicken, no lamb or pork, no milk, no cheese; on occasion, they might have an egg; more frequently, a small portion of white-meat fish. They eat no sweets unless they are grain- or fruit-based. That rules out sugar.

Carol Louro, a Kushi disciple who teaches macrobiotics in the New Bedford area, likes to point out that a regimen is not a culinary straitjacket. Quoting Mr. Kushi, she says, "Sometimes you have to have the apple pie."

Apple pie aside, what macrobioticians do eat are great quantities of whole grains, especially brown rice, the staple product, as well as millet, barley, oats, corn, buck-wheat, etc.

The diet also includes green, leafy vegetables such as kale and spinach, as well as round and root vegetables such as turnips, cabbage, radishes, and cauliflower.

Black beans, lentils, tofu and chickpeas make up the rest, along with a variety of tasty seaweeds such as nori and kombu and wakame.

Now that's not the stuff you will be likely to whip up for your backyard barbeque, but in the hands of an imaginative chef such as Carol Louro, these foods can be compelling, filling, and even addictive.

They can also be incredibly good for you, and by extension, for the world, which was the point of Mr. Kushi's lecture.

But those are not the foods of American culture.

Instead, most of us bombard our bodies with substances that have little relationship to natural needs, with easy-to-prepare, highly processed foods mass-produced and laced with chemical additives our cells can't recognize or robbed by the refining process of all nutritional value.

As parents, we recoil in horror as our children suffer from sugar highs or caffeine overloads or become bloated on sweetened white breads and cereals.

We laugh at people who are addicted to junk foods like Twinkies or Krispy Kremes.

But we all know too many people with sharp mood swings, sudden bursts of anger, attention deficits, high anxiety. We don't need to be nutritionists to suspect that the origin of many of these behaviors can be found in the ordinary diet.

We also know too many cancer victims, diabetics and heart patients.

We suspect many of these cases didn't just happen.

Folks who have cancer, or are recovering from cancer or worrying about cancer were in the audience the other night to hear Mr. Kushi, including at least two people who attribute their recovery from the disease to their macrobiotic regimens.

We are not qualified to say whether a radically healthy diet can help fight a disease as dreadful as cancer.

But there is little doubt that a radically bad diet can bring on cancer, as well as a host of other ills.

I'm also convinced that one day soon, the question of what Americans eat and how it is engineered, manufactured and processed will become an issue for public discussion and debate as we begin to examine our culture and its excesses more carefully.

It is a discussion the Mr. Kushi launched in his own gentle way in this country many years ago and continued in New Bedford the other night.

Carol Louro says he plans to return in November to continue his teaching in greater depth.

His message is worth listening to, even on the Fourth of July, maybe especially on the Fourth of July.

CHAPTER 6

THE IMPACT OF FOOD

Here is a story about how you can become too rigid in your thinking and eating. In the early years of having the center, there was a cook from Portugal named Carlos who came to teach. One day we were at the grocery store together and he picked up a bunch of red beets and said, "Aren't these beet tops beautiful?"

I immediately exclaimed, "We shouldn't be eating a lot of beets on a macrobiotic diet!"

"Well," Carlos said, "They're better than those muffins you were eating."

Having him say that to me helped me realize that I was being too rigid in my diet and then binging. We need to pay attention to our food choices, especially those we choose to binge on. We need to pay attention to what foods hurt different organs, what foods help different organs, and how food can affect our positive thinking. To know what foods are affecting us we must self-reflect. By saying this, I do not mean we should be hard on ourselves. There are reasons we make different choices, good and bad.

The food we eat has such an important impact on not only our physical health, but also our emotions and how we think, act, and choose to live. Having said this, moderation is what needs to be achieved when choosing foods to help balance health and emotions. Please try to eat a variety of foods—not only what kind of foods, but how we prepare them. We must cut vegetables in different styles every day and add different grains, beans and vegetables to our rice, soups, vegetable, and seaweed dishes. When we eat brown rice for our minds, or want to practice chewing, try practicing three times a week. Make it easy, don't be hard on yourself.

On the macrobiotic diet we eat brown rice that we cook ourselves. Many students at class were used to white rice, but when they started eating brown rice they noticed and felt the difference. Not only the improvement with their health but also with their emotions and how they were thinking. They enjoyed the flavor of the brown rice, as well as hearing about its benefits. Their favorite topic seemed to be chewing each mouthful fifty to one hundred times and emptying their minds. They noticed how they had better judgement dealing with the difficulties in their lives. As they chewed they would become more grounded and their thinking was clearer and calmer.

Yes, we become imbalanced off and on in life because of situations in our personal lives and also our food choices. That is a fact. But when we try and practice a simpler or cleaner diet our thinking and judgement improves and our fear lessens. Michio always said, "Sing a happy song every day!" We learn to be there for family and friends. We all need each other at different times in our lives. Our minds are open to so much positive, happy energy when we eat well, and new adventures become interesting.

Back in the 1970s, the macrobiotic community was eating way too much rice. It was half of what we ate back then. Okay, guess what made us too tight (yang)? And then we would binge big time (yin)! We laugh when we reminisce about that. Oh well. I think you had to be there, right?

It is important to pay attention to our thinking when we cook. The reason is that our energy goes into the food we prepare. Try and pay attention to energy when you enter a restaurant or when you are sitting near different people. Feel the energy, and pay attention to how you feel. Our energy is important not only to ourselves, but also to everyone around us. How you cook is important to your emotions. Learn to empty your mind and put out good thoughts before you begin cooking. Having a peaceful mind is beneficial for yourself as well as those who will eat your food.

The way you handle food will change its energy, so be gentle. When pouring broth or liquid into a pot, pour gently. When stirring, use a wooden spoon and try stirring in one direction, whichever direction you feel comfortable with. Don't mix or mash food in a chaotic or violent way. Also, try not to bang the spoon on the edge of the pan. Instead, gently use another spoon to scrape the food off.

Having said all this, what we use to cook is also very important. Use pots and pans that are made from stainless steel, ceramic, and glass. Avoid Teflon and aluminum. Don't cook in pans in which meat has previously been cooked. Cast iron pans are okay to use, but not every day. Because cast iron is very strong, cooking in it every day can make us too tight (yang). It is not good to cook in a microwave at all. Even warming food in a microwave is not advised. Electrical appliances are not advised for cooking; rather a gas stove is highly recommended.

In macrobiotic cooking we strive to make balance. The foods you put together and the way you cook affect the energy of your meal. For example, don't cover greens while cooking them because they will lose their "up" energy. Steam rises up and greens grow upward, which is yin. You want your greens to stay yin. By using a variety of cooking styles you will create balance.

Macrobiotic cooking relates to the seasons of the year. It is important in all seasons to have five colors and five flavors in the food presentation. Cooking that way gives movement in our bodies. Important principles in the macrobiotic way of life are cooking locally grown food and eating the vegetables that are in season. The way we cut and prepare our vegetables is also important. By cutting vegetables differently their flavors are different. When we cut onions in crescent moons, the onions taste sweet. Cutting the onion in rounds is also sweet. When you dice an onion, the flavor is more pungent.

When cooking carrots always use the very top and dice it into small pieces because lots of nutrients are in those pieces. When cooking with broccoli, also use the stems, not just the florets.

Yes, the macrobiotic way entails a lot of cooking, but the more we cook the easier it gets. When we experience the benefits that it gives us, our motivation to keep cooking is maintained.

When you are in good health you may eat 80% on the diet and 20% off. When we say 20% off the diet, we still don't eat any meat or dairy. Eating out is fine—just try and keep it simple, like pasta with the vegetables of the day, or a small portion of fish. But, if you are on a healing diet, eating out is not advised for a while.

I feel the most difficult part of the macrobiotic diet is satisfying our sweet cravings. I have always been a big fruit eater. I make desserts with barley malt and rice syrup. I also drink apple cider with kuzu to help me to not visit my favorite coffee shop and buy muffins.

I started eating the macrobiotic diet when I was expecting my youngest son, John. Therefore as a child, macrobiotic food was the only food he knew. When he was about five years old all my children went to a birthday party together. When they got home John was excited. He said, "Mom! There were these candies! They were all different colors. They were so delicious, I don't know why no one else was eating them. Everyone else was playing while I ate the candy! They were round and had a letter on them, but I can't remember what it was."

His older brother Chris said, "The letter was M, Johnny—THEY WERE M+M'S!"

"Oh yeah," said John, "It was an M."

I felt pretty guilty that John didn't even know what an M+M was. The next day he was very sick. Apparently he had eaten the whole bowl himself! Understanding our bodies, the reason John got sick is that his body was strong and he was discharging the sugar he had consumed. When people start on the macrobiotic diet to help strengthen their organs after years on the Standard American Diet, they often have strong discharges which are good to help clear out toxins from the body.

A balanced lifestyle is the best lifestyle; no one is perfect. When you begin a macrobiotic diet it is very helpful to see a macrobiotic counselor to learn what your condition is like. That is, where your weaknesses are, if you are too yin or too yang. Then you can learn what foods to choose to create balance for your condition.

If someone has an illness and is under the care of a macrobiotic counselor, meaning they are getting dietary advice from them, then they should consider having an experienced, certified, macrobiotic cooking teacher cook for them or at least guide them. The counselor will usually give the names of macrobiotic cooks that they can use. It is important to use a qualified cook to not only make the basic food, but also the medicinal dishes and drinks properly. Some illnesses can cause discharges from the stagnation in the body, but a qualified cook can prepare remedies to help calm and slow down this effect.

The cook communicates with the counselor closely, and the diet is gradually widened. The reason is that no one can eat strictly for a long period of time.

There are no "food saints." We can't feel embarrassed about our food choices. But, we must learn to self-reflect and pay attention to not only our health, but also our thinking. I think that if we take the time to practice chewing well and eating well (or at least better), then we will see how our effort is worthwhile. How else will we know if something can help us unless we try?

If we eat consciously we can self-reflect on our thinking and practice the "art of living." When we become aware of our feelings we can develop a more meaningful life. Our intuition opens. We develop a more generous spirit. We become appreciative of the blessings that come our way. It is easy to learn to talk to people in all walks of life. Why? Because we see and hear their heart. We have a sense of humor and most importantly we practice self-reflection. Our worry lessens and we don't back away from what we want in life—good things and happy situations.

When Joe and I were traveling in Portugal with friends, some of them were feeling bad for us during meals. As they were eating meat and different Portuguese foods they would say, "Oh, it's too bad you can't eat this!"

"No," Joe said, "It's not that we *can't* eat that food, we don't *want* to eat that food." When we consciously make our own choices, we are in charge of our destiny.

In my opinion the most important concept of macrobiotics is the philosophy—I feel that the more we try to understand it, the more we will learn to love ourselves, our families, our friends, our neighbors, and all of nature. The macrobiotic philosophy is also about learning how to be a comfort to others, to listen, and to have compassion and empathy. This way of being will spread, and can eventually spread into world peace.

It is important which foods you choose to eat, but also it's important *how* you eat them. With this, I would like to tell a story about Lino Stanchich.

I didn't know Lino, but he looks exactly like my grandfather. Because I had seen his picture I went to see him lecture. I was totally taken aback, in a good way, that the resemblance wasn't just in his physical appearance, but in his mannerisms as well. When I returned home from the Macrobiotic Summer Conference in Vermont where I saw him speak, my phone rang. I answered and heard, "Hello. I am looking for Carol Louro." It was Lino! I was shocked. He wanted to give a lecture at our center. On one hand I was very excited and on the other I was very nervous.

I told Michio how I felt and he asked, "Why, Carol?"

"Because of how Lino eats and how we eat!" He was known as a very conscious eater who chewed every mouthful one hundred times. When he got here he was so nice to be with and very informative.

When I showed Michio the photograph of my grandfather he said, "You and Lino related."

I must say that when I showed the picture to Lino he couldn't believe it either. "He even wears his hat and stands like me!" he said. When Lino came to New Bedford I introduced him to my father and cousins and they too couldn't believe the resemblance to my grandfather, John. In fact, Lino's family was on the island of St. Michael in the Azores at the same time as my family. Interesting!

Lino was known for teaching about how we eat, specifically how we chew. I am fortunate that Lino has allowed me to include his inspirational story in my book. Here is Lino's chapter about chewing and how he changed negativity into positivity.

CHAPTER 7

MY LIFE TRANSFORMATION: THANK YOU PAPA

By Lino Stanchich

In 1943, during World War II, my father, Antonio Stanchich, while serving on an Italian ship in Greece, was taken prisoner by the Germans and sent to a Nazi forced-labor concentration camp in Germany, where all the prisoners were forced into hard labor. At gunpoint, the men were forced to work outdoors, indoors in a factory, and on farms doing rough manual labor regardless of the weather.

That German winter was bitterly cold. The primitive barracks were poorly heated with broken windows, clothing was thin and inadequate, and the food sub-standard. In the morning the prisoners received a cup of herbal-chicory "coffee" and one slice of bread. For lunch and dinner they had a meager bowl of soup made of potatoes and some other vegetable, a grain or bean, and occasionally a bit of meat. My father said, "I was cold most of the time and hungry all the time." Inmates died daily. Deaths from infections, diseases, malnutrition, and exposure to the elements increased constantly. Life was a constant fight for survival.

One cold day, when my father was thirsty, he spontaneously kept the cold water in his mouth to warm it and intuitively "chewed" it for a while, about twenty-five times, before swallowing. Later, when the weather and the water was especially cold, he chewed it fifty times! And he discovered something that would save his life.

Aside from quenching my father's thirst, the water actually seemed to give him energy and provide warmth. At first he felt it must be his imagination. Eventually he realized that chewing water fifty times or more did indeed give him more energy and warmth. Puzzled, he asked himself how plain water could impart such a miracle. The fact was that the well chewed water, warmed in his mouth, gave him more vitality and he was not about to argue the point. He was determined to survive this horrendous wartime existence and return to his beloved family and home.

My father experimented by chewing his food fifty times a mouthful. Then he tried 75, 100, 150, 200, even up to 300 times or more. He determined that the magical *minimum* number of chews was 150 and the more he chewed, the more energy he had. The morning and noon meals were restricted in time, but the evening meal was not. Therefore, in the evening he could chew food and water as much and as long as he liked.

My father's technique was simple: Put one tablespoon of food or water in the mouth and count your chews. See how many chews you can do before swallowing. Eat slowly and calmly. He enthusiastically told his shipmates of his technique, yet most scoffed at his discovery, saying they wanted to swallow the soup warm immediately as they were so hungry. However, two friends became interested in these chewing experiments and joined my father in his eating sessions. Comparing notes, the three men confirmed that this chewing technique did give them more vitality. And they also felt warmer, less hungry, and more optimistic of their survival. Chewing well seemed to instill greater inner confidence, strengthening hope and resolve to endure.

In 1945, after two years in the Nazi labor camp, my father and his fellow prisoners were liberated by the U.S. Army. Of his crew of thirty-two from the Italian ship, only three men survived: my father, and the two men who joined him in his practice of chewing.

In time my father, skinny, but alive, came home to us in Fiume-Rijeka, formerly part of Italy, then Yugoslavia, now Croatia.

The following year, when I was 14, while on a family picnic, my father told me of his labor-camp eating experience. He attributed his survival exclusively to chewing. He gave me some important advice, saying: "If you are ever weak, cold, or sick, chew each mouthful 150 times or more." I never forgot those words, even though we had plenty of food and I was in good health.

Yet, 1949 found Yugoslavia in political turmoil. The communist government forbade Italian citizens to leave Yugoslavia and enter Italy. Many who opposed the communist government tried to escape Yugoslavia. I was one of them. I wanted to join my father in Italy. On March 10, 1949, I was captured at the Italian border and sentenced to two years of hard labor in a communist so called, "re-education" concentration camp. Now, at 17, I too became a prisoner.

My prison experience was extremely difficult, if not as horrible as my father's. The diet was similar to the one he had described: one bread roll with chicory coffee in the morning, a bowl of soup, usually with barley and beans, at noon; and the same in the evening. Once a week the soup included some meat. If there were twenty beans in the soup, I considered the meal a good one. Like my father, I was hungry most of the time.

Also like my father, I chewed my food and bread and salt sent from my mother, as my father had taught, 150 times or more, and I introduced an important feature: I chewed with my eyes closed. This way I could "escape" my depressing surroundings. Closing my eyes also internalized my energy. By not looking outward, my energy went inward, strengthening me more.

My experience in the concentration camp affected me deeply. The lighthearted, jovial young boy that I had been, became a hardened, tough man. When I arrived home in 1951, looking much older than my 19 years, my brother remarked, "If I didn't know you and saw you in a dark street, I would give you my wallet without your even asking for it."

The next year my family thankfully was allowed into Italy, and in 1953 we immigrated to the United States, where food was plentiful. I went into the restaurant business with my brother. Without any fear of starvation, I abandoned my chewing regime.

The years passed and in 1969, I began to suffer the effects of my high-stress life. I was startled to realize that I was digging my own grave with my fork! I tried many diets, from raw foods to fruit-only, from high-protein to lacto-vegetarian. The diets all worked to varying degrees, but didn't last long.

Then I discovered Macrobiotics, seeking the teachings of renowned Michio Kushi of Boston who taught phenomenal aspects of nature, the human body, organ functions, the healing power of whole foods, and spiritual development. Nutrition and health foods became my main interest and my lifelong, fulfilling career as a macrobiotic counselor, author, and educator. I became energized, positive, healthy, grateful, more loving and kind…. spiritually minded.

I continue to experiment and discover many things about eating and chewing. Magic happens when I practice calm, thorough chewing. Numerous students and friends have recounted how their lives have improved tremendously since they began eating in this conscious manner. The main ingredients for creating miracles are right under our noses – three times a day. Our food and the way we select it, cook it and eat it powerfully affects our lives, as well as the survival of this beautiful planet.

I lovingly pass along to you the advice my father gave me long ago on a picnic in Yugoslavia. "If ever you are weak, cold, or sick," he said, "chew each mouthful 150 times or more." This advice has been proven to work. It could help save thousands around the world who are starving, suffering, or ill.

After learning *what* to eat and *how* to eat properly, people began to improve and to heal themselves – often of "terminal" illnesses. Experience shows that healthy people who practice conscious chewing frequently feel the benefits after just one meal. Some report that they even feel euphoric and elated. Chewing will help those who eat any diet. However, the people who eat a balanced and well-organized whole grain-based macrobiotic, vegetarian, vegan, or plant-based diet will experience the most positive health results. Macrobiotics provides an organized and nutritionally sound program with detailed food selection, menu planning, and cooking knowledge.

For the past fifty years, I have counseled thousands of people who suffered diseases of mind and body, and who had tried various health programs and diets, still searching for greater healing, vitality, and fulfillment.

Macrobiotics has been profoundly rewarding to me, both as a practitioner on the personal level and as a teacher to others. This natural program helped me not only survive, but thrive. My wife, Jane, and I have traveling throughout the United States and Europe, visiting macrobiotic centers founded by visionaries such as our dear friend and cancer-survivor, Carol Louro, of Massachusetts. Studying and following the macrobiotic diet and natural lifestyle, I am vital and healthy, living now to age 88 in excellent health, optimistic about my future, productive, and enjoying life!

If we are to nurture our bodies and our planet, we must change our habits. America is 43rd in health worldwide. We can do much better! First, let us reflect on our eating habits. Consider the changes you want to make in your life. The time has come to adopt a way of eating that is ecological, healthful, nonviolent, and balanced. The only way to absorb such a diet is to eat it properly, a skill that few of us learned as children. You will also discover that eating well is a powerful way to love yourself and be the best you can be.

May we grow together in consciousness and save our Mother Earth before it is too late. May we love ourselves enough to give our minds and bodies the healthiest foods to heal and balance us emotionally, physically and spiritually. May you, my Friend, actualize your life's dream as you enjoy health, happiness, and peace in the realization of your fullest potential.

Happy chewing!
Lino

CHAPTER 8

A HEALING JOURNEY

By Phil Carney

December 27, 2000 was clear and crisp in South Dartmouth, Massachusetts. Kathy and I were packing to go skiing in Colorado and excited about the house we'd rented in Frisco, close to Copper Mountain, Breckenridge, Keystone and Arapahoe Basin, and not too long a drive to Vail and Beaver Creek. We planned to be away for three months, and were looking forward to fresh tracks on white powder.

At about 9:30 a.m., I got a call from our local medical center reminding me that I still needed to get some blood work done to complete a physical I had earlier, and would I come in that morning. I drove to the center, gave them a couple of vials, and then went home to tell Kathy I was going to Fairhaven to meet with my little brother, Nick. While I was on the road, Kathy called to tell me that the nurse practitioner wanted me to phone her right away. I was in front of the medical center so I pulled in to the parking lot and went to see her. Linda, the NP, was shocked to see me there so quickly. I told her I was close by and I thought I just stop in. But as I'm looking at her, I could see her eyes well up and she started to cry. I held her hand and told her everything would be OK. Plus, how bad could it be? (Little did I know.) Linda regained her composure and said "we think you have leukemia." I'd heard of leukemia but really didn't know what it was, and didn't feel any symptoms. I thought this was just a temporary condition, they'd give me some medicine, and I'd be fine. Linda made an appointment with an oncologist for the next day, and I went home to tell Kathy.

Kathy was surprised when I came back to the house. She asked if there was something wrong and I said that they thought I had leukemia. After each of us said "are you OK?" I told her I was late to meet Nick and had to go.

A few things helped get me through that morning. The first really was "ignorance is bliss" because I had no idea what was in store. The second is that I'm the type of person who doesn't get upset until I know there's a problem. (There was plenty of time for that later.) And the third is that I was going to spend the day with Nick, so my mind would be on other things.

While I was blissfully ignorant, my wife looked up leukemia and therapies. So when I came home, Kathy said she thought she knew what kind of leukemia I had. I looked at her is if she had two heads. How could she possibly know what kind of leukemia I had? And who knew there was more than one kind? After I tried not to tell her she was crazy, I reminded her that we were seeing the oncologist the next day and that he'd give us more information. She said "just for the record, I think you have chronic myeloid leukemia." As nicely as I could, I asked her how in the world she came up with that. And very matter-of-factly she said she was guided to a website, and she did some research on a very promising new drug. I love my wife dearly but I couldn't believe what she was saying.

The next day we went to the oncologist and, as we were having a conversation, he said he wanted to refer me to Dana-Farber, a cancer hospital in Boston. He also said he was pretty sure I had CML. Kathy, who's sitting in the back of the room, said "is that chronic myeloid leukemia?" The oncologist stared at her and asked if she were a doctor. She said "no, but could you tell me the latest STI-571?" At this point I'm praying that he doesn't ask her how she knows about this. He pulled out a medical journal and showed her the most recent research, and said that because STI-571, a targeted drug therapy for CML, has been so successful in trials, the FDA was going to rush approval. Odds were good that it would be available in July, 2001. This was December, 2000, and my white blood cells count was 56,000. Normal is between 4,000 and 11,000. I figured all I needed to do was wait six months, take the pill, and everything would be fine.

We met with the oncologist at Dana-Farber in mid-January, 2001, who discussed some existing trials, but recommended against entering any one of them because of potential side effects. Instead, he started me on hydroxyurea, an oral chemotherapy which he hoped would get me through until July. Still fairly clueless, I asked if we could go skiing. He said taking a few runs would be fine, but was pretty surprised when I said we wanted to go to Colorado for a few months. He agreed only if I'd get weekly blood draws and fly home right away if there were a problem. We left the next day.

Initially, the hydroxyurea worked well, and there was little change in the white blood cell count. As requested, I went to the local clinic in Frisco every week and skied the rest of the day. In one of my ski classes, a woman introduced herself as a nurse from the clinic and said "maybe I shouldn't be telling you this, but we're all so excited when you come in. All the nurses and doctors gather around to look at your blood because we've never seen anything like it before." I told her I was glad to be of service.

When we came home in March, my counts were still pretty stable, and then all of a sudden, they weren't. They climbed steadily into the 60,000, 70,000 and 80,000 range. The oncologist did all that he could to find a bone marrow donor for me, afraid that I wouldn't last until July. He was concerned that my counts would reach 100,000, a "blast crisis," where life expectancy from then on was typically about six months.

Kathy began researching as many alternative therapies as she could. She'd hear about people who'd been dying, no longer helped by conventional medicine, and later cured by eastern practitioners. She'd take (drag) me to meet with these healers. In every case, we knew the patients and I believe that the alternative therapies worked for them. But somehow, the therapies didn't resonate with me.

Although she didn't say much, I could feel Kathy's anxiety and knew I needed to get away by myself. By this point I was sleeping for a day and a half and awake for half a day. I had no energy and couldn't walk to the end of the block. I knew I was dying and didn't need to be reminded by sensing her fear. I told her that I was going to visit a cousin in Canada. She asked when we were going and I told her, maybe not so kindly, that I was going alone. Her recollection of this time is that we were basically hissing at each other, and that I was looking for garlic and a cross before I'd talk to her.

Undaunted, Kathy kept looking at ways to keep me alive. Through a series of fortunate events, she heard about macrobiotics. After her initial skepticism of "why would anybody eat that way?" she dug in a little more and read about a lot of people who turned their illnesses around. On March 29 (my birthday,) she slipped a piece of paper under the door where I was sleeping. "I know I said I wouldn't do talk about this anymore, but read this and let me know what your think."

Although I didn't want to admit it, macrobiotics made sense. Especially the "let food be thy medicine and medicine be thy food" part. There was a macrobiotic center in Becket, MA, in the beautiful Berkshire mountains. They had a week-long program called "Way to Health" which started that Sunday afternoon (April Fool's Day.) This included three healthy meals a day, cooking classes, lectures, consultations, and if you wanted, oriental diagnoses. I told my wife I was still going away for the weekend and wouldn't be able to get there until Sunday night. She didn't care. She'd made the sale.

When we arrived, my white blood cell count was 96,000, almost at a blast crisis. I was extremely weak, slept through most of the lectures, and only got out of bed to eat. I'd made a commitment to the oncologist to get my blood drawn at a local clinic, and went there Wednesday morning. I'd had eight macrobiotic meals by then – dinner on Sunday, three on Monday and Tuesday, and breakfast on Wednesday. I was flabbergasted when they told me my white blood cell count was down to 54,000.

Eating macrobiotically was a major transition for Kathy and me. I loved meat and my favorite food was pizza, and Kathy liked anything with dairy, flour and sugar. The first few days of eating plant-based food felt like we were eating cardboard. It had the consistency of food, but no taste. About the third day, though, we could actually sense the sweetness of the squash and onions as our palates began to be cleansed of the sugar, salt and spices we were used to.

We came home April 6, and the temperature was still fairly cool. Kathy suggested we try taking a walk again, and bundled me up in a jacket, scarf and gloves. The month before, I barely made it out of the house. I couldn't believe it when I realized we'd been walking for more than a mile.

While I had a lot more energy, I was beginning to look skeletal. When I started eating macrobiotically, I weighed close to 200 lbs. (I'm six feet tall,) but was losing weight rapidly. We'd be warned that this would happen, as our bodies were able to discharge fats and toxins because we're no longer ingesting them. We'd also been told that after a while, we'd regain some of our weight, but probably not to where it'd been before.

One of the hardest things about leaving the Kushi Institute was that we'd have to cook for ourselves. While Kathy was never a big meat eater, she'd never liked beans, either. When one of the macrobiotic counselors asked her what her favorite beans were, she said "jelly beans." I liked beans, but never cooked them. Things were even more complicated because Kathy thought that if she made anything wrong, it would kill me. So for the first couple of weeks, I made the meals.

Then a miracle happened and we found a certified macrobiotic chef who lived five miles from our house. Carol Louro literally saved our lives. She cooked three meals a week for us and invited us to her weekly cooking classes. After a few weeks, I saw Kathy cooking rice and chopping vegetables in the kitchen, and I'm sure I heard the angels sing "hallelujah!"

When we went to Dana-Farber a few weeks later, I'd probably lost 20 lbs. I'd had blood drawn in the morning and the resident fellow checked the results on her computer before my appointment with the oncologist. She kept saying "there's been a mistake," and asked for the results again. My white blood cell count was down to 5,600, well within normal range.

The resident asked if I'd done anything differently and I told her that I changed the way I ate. She updated the doctor and when he came in, he was upset that I was so thin. His concern was that he was trying to find a bone marrow donor and that I needed some fat reserves to make it through the operation and recovery. What I realized, though, was that the diet was working and I no longer needed a transplant.

Even with normal white blood cell counts, my doctor convinced me that I should take advantage of the targeted drug therapy, STI-571, which was branded as Gleevec. The pharmacist at CVS told me I was the first person in New England to receive it. I know that, without a doubt, I would have died without the guidance of my macrobiotic counselors and the healing diet they recommended. Years later, when the leukemia remained undetectable, I decided (with my doctor's knowledge but against his advice) to stop the chemotherapy. Twenty years after the initial diagnosis, the CML is still undetectable.

A year after the leukemia was reversed, Kathy and I decided to travel again. We were committed to staying on the diet, though, so we'd call ahead to find places that were receptive to our requests. We had some great experiences.

Our first trip was to England and Scotland, and we called hotels in London and Edinburgh to make sure they could accommodate us. We emailed what we could/couldn't eat, and provided them some sample recipes. We brought over a small "starter kit" of some condiments, including umeboshi plums, gomashio and lots of kukicha tea bags. In London, the hotel had a main dining room and a pub on the premises. The head chef met with us and said he considered it an honor – and a challenge – to serve us. The food was delicious, and each night the chefs and the servers made sure we were satisfied. Many of them were interested in why we changed the way we ate, and talked about a friend or relative that had cancer or a heart condition. They wanted to know if changing their life style would help them, too.

When we described our diet to the head chef at our hotel in Scotland, he kept nodding and telling us the diet sounded very Japanese. We asked how he knew so much about macrobiotics. It turns out that he won the award for the best recipe on how to use soy sauce for the Kikkoman Soy Sauce contest, and that part of the prize was a trip to Japan! The chefs were very proud of their plant-based creations and their presentation was always beautiful. Every night we'd get our special meals and there were always people who complained that they didn't see what we were eating on the menu!

Socially, eating with our friends was a challenge. Some people stopped inviting us to dinner, but others included us when they knew we'd bring our own food. Invariably, other guests would ask to share ours "just to have a taste." Now we have a healthy gourmet group that meets regularly, and the number of people who participate is growing all the time.

In addition to teaching and cooking for us, Carol introduced us to macrobiotic counselors, including Michio Kushi, the person responsible for bringing macrobiotics to the United States. In the macrobiotic world, he was a rock star. I was blessed to have Michio as my first counselor. He was a quiet, gentle man who would look at my face and hands, contemplate what he saw, and tell me what I could do to improve my condition.

At first, my diet was very restrictive. No meat, dairy, refined flour or sugar, and no alcohol. There were foods that I thought were healthy that were on the "occasional" or "avoid" lists until I got better. I steadily improved, with more energy and a much more positive attitude following his recommendations.

I rarely cheated on the diet, but I remember we were driving home from Colorado and stopped at a service center on the highway. The only food available was at a Panera's. Michio had always told us that when there weren't other choices, "the universe provides," and to eat as well as we could within the diet. While there were soups and sandwiches available, I was craving a bagel and coffee, and decided to go for it. On the way home, we called Carol to ask if we could pick up some food. As soon as I walked in the door, Carol said "you had coffee." I immediately denied it, but she persisted. Plus, she knew she was right because Kathy couldn't stop laughing.

One good thing about dealing with a macrobiotic counselor is that you don't have to lie about anything. They know that cancer craves sugar and stimulants (e.g., caffeine) and have heard it all before. They're trained to help you get your body back in balance, so if you go "off the bus" they'll work with you to get back on. No judgment.

Speaking of counselors, Carol had many of them come to her home, and I had the privilege of working with experts like Marc Van Cauwenberghe, Ed Esko, Tom Monte, and Bettina Zumdick. Each has had a positive impact on my health. I continue to seek their advice to this day.

But not everything has gone smoothly since the leukemia came under control. Two and a half years after my initial diagnosis, I had a meeting with Michio right after I was told that the CML was still "undetectable." I was sure that Michio would widen my diet and include some more "normal" foods. Instead, he tightened the diet up even more. As I was leaving, he put his hand on my shoulder and told me that if the doctors said I had another cancer, not to be alarmed, and that we could take care of it.

I had no idea how I could possibly have anything else, having been so strict on the diet. Plus, I was frustrated (i.e., angry) that I had even less variety than when I came. But two months later, after a bone marrow aspiration, I was diagnosed with multiple myeloma. This is what Michio saw.

This was the beginning of realizing that my health journey would be more of a roller coaster than a straight line. Because two years after that diagnosis, I found out I had prostate cancer. Three unrelated cancer diagnoses in five years. I have no idea why. I'd worked in a shoe factory as a teenager and used toxic bottom paint on sail boats, but I'm sure a lot of other people did too. It could be for any number of reasons. But twenty years later, I know that I wouldn't have survived any of these diseases if I hadn't found macrobiotics. While managing my health is challenging, I continue to be mindful of what I eat and drink and am extremely grateful for the very full life that I have.

I'm constantly reminded of what Hippocrates said in 400 B.C. – "let food be thy medicine and medicine be thy food." Words to live by.

CHAPTER 9

WHAT IS MACROBIOTICS?

Preparing to write this book I went through many old notes and macrobiotic writings. One of my favorites is by John David Mann, written back in the early 1980s. I am so pleased he allowed me to share it with you.

What is Macrobiotics?
By John David Mann

Macrobiotics is a way of living with respect for the physical, biological, emotional, mental, ecological and spiritual order of our daily lives. Beginning with a reorientation of everyday eating, using whole natural foods of highest quality and simple, more traditional methods of preparation, macrobiotic living means striving to learn the art of *balance* in everything we do. Macrobiotic living means accepting responsibility for putting and keeping our lives in harmony, within ourselves, our families and communities, and with society, with nature and with God.

Although macrobiotic living can help restore and maintain your personal health, it is not a particular form of therapy or medicine. Yet it may be pursued while you are using any type of traditional or even modern medicine, if this is necessary. Macrobiotic living can help restore and maintain your spiritual direction and faith, but it is not a religion. Yet it is compatible with any traditional religion.

Macrobiotic eating does not mean adhering to one set, unchanging "diet." It may mean eating in a more regulated, simple way, or in a more broadly varied way, depending upon your needs, preferences and circumstances, all of which change over time. Macrobiotic eating means gaining your own understanding of how different foods affect you, and it means choosing, preparing and consuming your food and drink with an active sense of reverence for life.

What is Macrobiotic Counseling?

Macrobiotic counseling is not professional medical or nutritional advice. It is an educational process for reviewing your personal situation and helping introduce you to macrobiotic eating, thinking and living. The purpose of macrobiotic counseling sessions is to help you gain further insight into the reasons for your unhappiness or other problems, and to explore how macrobiotics may help you create a happier, healthier and more positive life. Additional factors that will help you achieve this reorientation include: a personal commitment to self-reflect and change; an active lifestyle rich in involving and rewarding interests; supportive and loving friends and family members; a sense of respect for nature, and your personal faith in God.

What is Macrobiotic Eating?

Regulating your daily eating and drinking is the most basic, practical way to change your condition. The food you eat becomes your blood, affecting the quality of your cells, tissues, organs and your mind. Properly nourished, your body, heart and mind can more easily cleanse and renew themselves. This can be a wonderful experience and an opportunity to learn more about yourself and the process of natural healing.

Macrobiotic eating uses whole, natural, unrefined foods and emphasizes home cooking, with simple methods of preparation and mild, natural seasonings. Whole cereal grains are the staple food; fresh vegetables (mostly cooked) are also used at nearly every meal; and a wide variety of other foods are used as additional side dishes, including beans, seeds, nuts and other protein-rich foods, soups, sea vegetables, fish (if desired), seasonal fruits, natural sugar-free and dairy-free desserts, and others.

CHAPTER 10

SELF-REFLECTION

When I think of the many different memories of my life, I tend not to think about my cancer. Sometimes it's like I've forgotten I went through it. At cooking class there was a woman with cancer going through some very tough times. After she left I said to Lorraine, "I just can't believe what she's going through."

"Carol, really!? You *DID* go through it!" she said with a very puzzled look on her face.

I said, "Oh, I forgot for a minute," and was completely shocked that I could have forgotten.

I told Marc about what happened, "I don't know how I could forget..."

With his Belgian accent he replied, "Yeah...it's because you are *completely* cured."

Reflecting on Marc's insightful comment makes me understand that we really do get healed by how we think.

Thinking back to my childhood, I realize that what influenced my thinking, firstly, was Lena with World War 2, her heartache, the atrocities that she experienced, and how she walked out of that with a warm and loving demeanor, pushing the sadness and hurt away. I remember my mother coming home from the open house at my school. She said, "Carol, your teacher says you get good marks in anything about World War 2." Having met so many people affected by war made me want to understand even more why this had happened to them.

Then there was being with musicians and professionals in the music field. I might add, not just being with them, but interacting with them in a very warm, emotional, loving manner. Most of them were at the top of their field. Seeing what was important to them, not the fact that they were great at what they did, play instruments, dance, and sing, but that they were humble, loved what they did, and had such close relationships. They were always proud of their colleagues and would complement each other. I never saw jealousy among any of them, only encouragement for one another. The philosophy was do what you do to the best of your ability, and most importantly know that it's not what you do, it's who you are and how you treat people. If one of the musicians was having difficulties, their musician friends would get together and discuss in depth how to help them. Love, friendship, and lighthearted sense of humor poured out of them. Seeing that left a big impression on me in my mind and heart. It was beautiful.

When my father stopped traveling for the sake of my brother and me, his local musician friends also helped and supported one another. As I grew older I realized the love and support they all had for each other. My father had a music store and his friends with music stores in and around the same local area all helped each other out, and shared instruments, music students, whatever anyone needed—very much a macrobiotic lifestyle.

When I got older, I spent many days with my Uncle Lou in his jewelry store. We would sit in the backroom, have coffee, and his friends who were mostly veterans would tell me a lot of stories of what they went through, but Uncle Lou didn't say much. My uncle was in Germany for three years and didn't disclose much until later in life. He was at my house every Sunday morning and started saying some things.

Now when I look back I feel God put me in the right places to become involved in macrobiotics and yes, it is the philosophy that I love about it. We all go through hard times in our lives and heartache, but it's important we are there for one another, and what a blessing it is to be able to open your heart to help people walk through their difficulties. I know it makes a big difference in our hearts and yes, it helps to promote peace. I feel blessed with my life, and am very happy to have known so many strong, brave, and loving people who by the way, were very loving to me.

After over forty years in macrobiotics one of the most special things about the experience is the people I've connected with. People I met in the very beginning, both counselors and people who attended our classes, are still in my life today. And not just as acquaintances, but as TRUE friends. I realize it's not the material things in life that make us happy, it's the people around us.

Recently Tom Monte and his wife Toby were a great comfort to me during difficult times, as was Bettina Zumdick who stayed with us and cooked for my family. Edward Esko and his wife Naomi came to visit Joe, my children, and me. Ed has always been a great friend and confidant. Today he is still encouraging me to do new things. Evelyn Harboun Miyaji, a great friend, was right there for me and helped cook for my husband when he was sick. I love eating at her and her husband's macrobiotic restaurant, Masao's Kitchen in Waltham, Massachusetts. Whenever friends go they bring back food for me!

I'm still in touch with Steve Gagné, Wendy Esko, and Joe Avoli even though they have all moved far away.

Edward Esko, Alex Jack, and Bettina Zumdick still invite me to lecture at macrobiotic summer conferences. I hadn't known Lawrence Kushi well, but I became friendly with him at a summer conference and we spent time talking and exchanging stories. I told him stories about his father and enjoyed doing it! I'm still in touch with Norio Kushi too.

A couple of years ago I was at a knitting group and a woman brought in a book, The Code to Joy. One of the authors was John David Mann. I saw it and exclaimed, "I know the author!"

Someone said, "Really? Did you see him speak somewhere?"

I told them that he used to work with me teaching macrobiotics. They were surprised to hear I knew him and someone asked if I would contact him to give a talk. Well, I reached out to him after not seeing him for many years and he was happy to hear from me, "Wow! A blast from the past! How are Joe and the children?" He was very warm and kind.

The reason I wanted to write this book is that I feel so blessed to have spent so much time with Lena. She opened my heart and mind to many of life's paths. Because of her, I ventured down the path that brought me to meet Michio and Aveline, become a macrobiotic teacher, and work with many colleagues who became dear friends and share the same dream of world peace.

By Ruby Louro

PHOTO SECTION

The Fairgrounds

Carol at the Fairgrounds with Ralph Heid in his performance outfit

Carl and me

My brother Carl and cousin Jane with our dog, Goldie

When I surprised my friend Michele (right) after returning
home from a summer of traveling with the fair

My grandfather, John Soares

Lino and Jane Stanchich (see the resemblance Lino has to my grandfather?)

I always loved how this family portrait, taken at a wedding, came out. The only problem was that my son, John, didn't make it into the picture. It always bothered me so years later I took it to a photo shop and had them add in a picture of John wearing his tux from prom. I happily showed it to him, and he said, "Great, Mom. Now I'm older than Aimee!" Aimee, in the center of the photo, is actually 3 years older than John, standing back left!

Top Row: John, Joe, and I
Bottom Row: Chris, Aimee, and Tracy

My parents, Lionel and Sara Soares

My parents (on the left) with my Uncle Lou and Aunt Issy

Joe and me

Lorraine and me in Vancouver, BC

Carol Louro

Edward Esko teaching at the East West Center of New Bedford in 1983

Michio Kushi, during the last lecture he gave in New Bedford

Our Family

Joe on our last trip to Portugal with Father Roy and our grandson, Joshua

Receiving the Aveline Kushi Award from Ed Esko in 2018

PART 2
The Recipes

When it comes to food, we all have certain tastes we prefer. Remember the story of Lorraine and me making the Sweet and Sour Tempeh? When cooking these recipes, please use your discretion to season the dishes to YOUR liking. However, please remember that seasoning your food on the lighter side is what I would always recommend. The same goes for the amounts of water used in grain, bean, and soup recipes. Depending on how much liquid may come out of the vegetables or how high the flame on your stove is, adjust the amounts of water to your own taste to make the food thinner or thicker.

Before beginning the recipe portion of the book, I would like to share the letter we would give to all newcomers who attended our cooking class:

Hello, Welcome to my Cooking Class,

My wish for my class is to help you create balance, which creates health, happiness and peacefulness, which leads to FREEDOM. We are always seeking balance through diet, spirituality, work and play.

Happiness cannot be wished for. It must be created within one's self, and in turn spread to all of those around us.

The peacefulness we begin to experience opens our 5 senses. We begin to see and feel the cycle of life, by loving nature, ourselves, other individuals, all animals, and also differences.

Life will at times bring us challenges. We will learn to use these challenges as a growing experience by creating new paths that will make us grow stronger and solve these challenges through peaceful means.

Together let's follow our dream!

Thank You for COMING,
In Peace and Love,

Joe & Carol Louro

Grains

Different varieties of brown rice include: short grain, medium grain, long grain, and sweet brown rice. There is also black and red rice that is to be used only occasionally. My favorite variety is medium grain brown rice. It is important to add a pinch of sea salt when cooking rice because it balances the grain. After cooking it is important to transfer rice from the metal pot to a wooden or glass bowl.

Brown Rice

For 1 cup of brown rice, use 1 ½ cups water.
For 2 cups of brown rice, use 3 cups water.

Wash the rice first. You may also soak it overnight or for an hour. Add rice to the pan and slowly add the water. It is important to pour gently for calming energy. Bring to a boil and add a pinch of sea salt. Lower the flame, cover, and simmer for 45 minutes. Please do not leave cooked rice in the pan, because of the energy of the metal. Place the cooked rice in a wooden or glass bowl.

Sweet Brown Rice with Squash

This recipe is very good for our stomach and spleen. It is also very relaxing and calming for the mind. If you have leftovers, they are good to use in a soup the next day.

Ingredients:
1 cup sweet brown rice
1¼ cup winter squash (butternut, acorn, or kabosha) cut into 1" pieces
3 cups water
Sea Salt

Preparation:

Place rice and squash in the pan. Gently add the water and bring to a boil. Keep in mind that the amount of liquid that comes out of the squash always differs, so use your own judgement to add more water if needed. Add a pinch of sea salt, lower the flame, cover, and simmer 45-50 minutes. When done, stir to blend and transfer to a wooden bowl.

Fried Rice

Ingredients:
3-4 cups cooked brown rice
1-2 tablespoons sesame oil or olive oil
1 tablespoon soy sauce
½ cup corn
¼ cup onions, cut small
½ cup sprouts
1 cup scallions, cut small
¼ cup carrots, cut small

Preparation:
Sauté onion until translucent, then add carrots and cook for about 2 minutes more. Add corn and sprouts. Cook another 3-4 minutes and add soy sauce and cooked rice to pan. Mix well. Add scallions and serve.

Brown Rice with Barley
This combination is very delicious in the hot summer months because it is light.

Ingredients:
2 cups brown rice
1/3 cup barley, soaked overnight
3 ½ cups water
Pinch sea salt

Preparation:
Place brown rice and barley in a pot. Slowly add the water. Bring to a boil. Add the pinch of sea salt, cover and turn down heat to a simmer for 40 minutes. You may use a flame deflector if you have one.

Millet and Squash
We use millet as a change from eating rice often. Also it is very delicious in soups or mixed with vegetables and formed into patties and fried.

Ingredients:
1 cup millet
1½ cup butternut squash, cut in large chunks
3 cups water
Pinch sea salt

Preparation:
Place millet, squash and water in a pot. Bring to a boil, add salt, cover and simmer 30-35 minutes or until water is all absorbed.

Millet with Cauliflower

Ingredients:
2 cups millet
1 cauliflower, cut up small
4 cups water
Pinch sea salt

Preparatoin:
Place millet, cauliflower, and water in a pot. Bring to a boil, then add pinch of sea salt. Cover, lower heat and simmer for about 35 minutes. When done, remove from the pot and mix together.

Gomashio

Gomashio is a wonderful condiment to have on your grains. You can buy it, but there's nothing like homemade. It is best to make enough to have in 1 week.

Ingredients:
2 ½ tablespoons sea salt
1 cup sesame seeds

Preparation:
Rinse and dry roast sesame seeds in a pan on the stove top, stirring frequently with a wooden spoon, until they are light brown and fragrant. When you can easily crush one between your fingers you know they are ready. Place in a suribachi. Then dry roast sea salt for 3-4 minutes the same way. Add to the suribachi and grind together until seeds are half crushed and coated with sea salt.

Suribachi
By Christin Ritz

Carol Louro

Tahini Noodles

Ingredients:
½ cup tahini
½ cup water
½ teaspoon umeboshi vinegar
1 tablespoon lemon juice
Soy sauce or sea salt to taste
Scallions, parsley, or chives—whichever you prefer for garnish
Brown rice noodles

Preparation:
Cook noodles as directed on package. When done, rinse thoroughly and set aside. Pour tahini into a suribachi slowly. Add the water and keep stirring with the pestle until creamy. Add the soy sauce, umeboshi vinegar, and lemon juice. When all mixed together, toss with the noodles, garnish, and enjoy.

SOUP

I love miso soup at lunch or dinner. Besides miso soups, other soups such as vegetable soups, bean soups, and broths are important for variety. I especially enjoy a hearty bean and kale soup in the evening. I loved when Joe and Aimee would make a kale and watercress soup in the winter on Sunday and the whole family would eat it with a good quality bread from a Portuguese bakery. Many foods are good memories.

Tips for making miso soup:

- When cooking miso soup dilute about ½ to 1 tsp per cup of broth.
- It is very important that after you add the diluted miso back into the soup you simmer it for 4-5 minutes, but never boil it.
- Grains and beans may also be added to the soups. Shitake mushrooms too!
- I like to make soups with watercress. Add the roots and leaves at the point you add the miso paste.
- Miso soup needs to be garnished before serving with scallions, chives, or parsley. The reason for this is that it lightens it up and balances out the salty broth.

Miso soup is very delicious, and important in the macrobiotic diet. In Japan it is a staple food. Fortunately in Western countries people are eating it and they know its nutritional importance to our health. Miso contains living enzymes that strengthen our digestion, and it also has protein, calcium, iron, and vitamin B. It is important that the soup not be boiled after the miso is added because that can destroy the enzymes. There are many different kinds of miso. Barley miso is my favorite, made from organic ingredients and naturally fermented for 24-36 months. This is called 2 year miso. Some different kinds of miso are:

- Barley Miso, also called Mugi miso. This is suitable for all year.
- Brown Rice Miso, also called Genmai miso. It is more suitable to have during the summer months.
- Other misos are sweet white and red misos, which are good in bean stews, fish stews, sauces and dressings. These are for occasional use.

On a root vegetable like a carrot, lotus root, or turnip, look at the point where the greens grow upward from, and the root grows downward from. This part of the plant has lots of nutrients and very strong energy. Finely cut up this part of the vegetable and add it to your soups to strengthen the organs. In my family we always make sure the kids get some of this in their soup dish.

Portuguese Kale Soup

Ingredients:
6-8 cups water
1 tablespoon olive oil
½ onion, diced
½ turnip, diced
½ cup carrots, diced
1 bunch of kale, chopped (also chop stems and set aside)
1 – 1 ½ cup cooked kidney beans
Sea salt

Preparation:
Sauté onions in olive oil. Place onions, turnips, and carrots in the pot, along with kale stems and 3 cups of water. Simmer for about 10 minutes, then add the cooked beans, kale leaves, and the rest of the water (you may use water from cooking the beans if there is any leftover). Continue cooking for 40-45 minutes. Add sea salt to taste and cook an additional 15 minutes. Serve with sourdough bread.

- *For variation, you may substitute cooked navy beans or chickpeas. I prefer kidney beans.*
- *You may also add cooked brown rice spiral pasta if desired.*

My Friend's Recipe for Portuguese Kale Soup

The Portuguese like to make large amounts of kale soup in large pans and eat it for 2-3 days. It seems to taste better the next day. They often invite people over or give some away to their family and neighbors.

Ingredients:

4 quarts vegetable broth
1 15.5oz can kidney beans, use the liquid and mash beans slightly
1 15.5oz can cannelli beans, use liquid as well
1-2 onions, cut large
2 carrots, cut large
1 bunch kale, sliced thin
3-4 small potatoes, diced, optional
Sea salt to taste
Black pepper to taste, optional
Green or red pepper, sliced, optional

Preparation:

When you slice the kale, separate the stems from the greens because they will be cooked separately. Put all the ingredients in a large stock pot, except for the kale greens (stems can go in), black pepper, and sea salt. Bring to a boil and simmer about 25 minutes. Add the kale greens and simmer an additional 20 minutes. In the last 10 minutes add the sea salt and black pepper.

Basic Miso Soup

Ingredients:

5-6 cups spring water
1 cup onions, sliced in crescent moons
1 small piece of wakame seaweed, about the size of half your thumb
½ cup carrots, cut into rounds
2 ½-3 tsp miso paste of any kind
Scallions or parsley, chopped

Preparation:

Rinse wakame seaweed, then soak in water for 20-25 minutes. Throw away the soaking water and thinly slice the wakame. Add the wakame and water to a soup pot and simmer for about 10 minutes. Then add the onions and carrots and simmer for about 5 minutes more. Remove 1 cup of hot soup broth and dilute the miso into it. Add the diluted miso back into the soup and simmer about 5 minutes more, but do not boil. When you serve add your scallion or parsley garnish.

Watercress Soup

Ingredients:

5 cups water
1" piece of wakame, soaked and sliced thin
1 medium onion, cut into crescent moons
1 cup carrots, cut into fans, or turnips, diced small
1 bunch watercress, stems and tops chopped separately
2 1/2 – 3 teaspoons miso
1 whole lemon, optional

Preparation:

Simmer wakame, onions, carrots, watercress stems, and whole lemon (if using) for 10-12 minutes. Add the watercress tops. Remove 1 cup of broth, dilute the miso in, and add back to the pot. Simmer 5-7 minutes more. If using the lemon, add it to the soup at the beginning, and at the end remove it gently so it does not break. If it does, it will make the soup extremely bitter.

Aimee's Vegetarian Split Pea Soup

Ingredients:

6 cups vegetable broth
2 cups dried green split peas, soaked overnight
1 medium onion, chopped
1 cup carrots, diced

2 celery stalks, chopped
½ teaspoon sea salt
1 clove minced garlic, optional
½ teaspoon dried basil, optional
¼ teaspoon ground cumin, optional
Ground black pepper, optional

Preparation:

In a large saucepan combine all ingredients except for the sea salt. Bring to a boil, cover, and turn down heat. Simmer for an hour or until peas are tender, stirring occasionally. Add salt and pepper, then simmer 10 minutes more. Optionally you can purée the soup, then return to the pan and heat 5 minutes more before serving. Garnish with scallions or parsley.

Squash Soup

Ingredients:

4-5 cups spring water
1 medium butternut squash, peeled and cut into small cubes
Wakame, size of half your thumb, soaked about 45 minutes and cut small (toss soaking water)
1 large onion, cut in crescent moons
Sesame oil
Sea salt
½ – 1 teaspoon per cup of water barley, sweet, or white miso
Scallions or parsley, chopped

Preparation:

Add squash to water and wakame. Bring to boil and simmer until soft. While squash is cooking, sauté the onion in a small amount of oil with a pinch of sea salt to bring out sweetness. Cook onions until caramelized. Add this to the soup pot with the squash. Simmer 5 minutes more. Purée, either by hand with a potato masher, or with an electric mixer. Then remove a cup of soup, place in suribachi and purée the the miso into it. Add it back into the soup and simmer 5-7 minutes more. When serving garnish with scallions or parsley.

Whole Lemon Soup

Ingredients:
2 stalks celery, diced
1 onion, sliced into crescent moons
½ cup string beans, diced
1 lemon, whole
2-3" piece wakame, soaked, drained, and cut small
5 cups water
2½ – 3 teaspoons white miso
Scallions or chives, finely cut

Preparation:
Put water in your soup pot with whole lemon and wakame. Simmer for 10 minutes. Add the onion, celery and string beans to the pan and simmer for 5-7 minutes more. Remove the lemon gently so it doesn't break. Remove a cup of broth and dissolve miso into it. Add miso back into soup and let simmer 3-5 minutes more. Garnish with scallions or chives and serve.

- *For this soup put the whole lemon in the pot while cooking. Don't cut it or zest it. The lemon taste will be flavorful but not overpowering. Remove the celery's strings before using.*

Minestrone Soup

Ingredients:
6 cups water
¼ cup barley, soaked overnight, optional
1/3 cup cooked chickpeas
½ cup cooked kidney beans
¼ cup black eyed peas, not cooked

Wakame, a piece the size of a postage stamp, soaked 45 minutes (toss soaking water)
1 onion, diced
2 summer squash, cut in rounds or squares
3 ears of corn, removed from the cob
3 stalks of celery, strings removed, diced
½ cup turnip, diced small
½ dry cup brown rice macaroni noodles or shells
1 teaspoon soy sauce
Umeboshi vinegar

Preparation:

Bring water, barley (if using), beans and wakame to a boil. Cover and simmer 30 minutes. In the meantime, separately boil noodles until done. Rinse noodles and set aside. Add vegetables and simmer another 12 minutes uncovered. Add cooked noodles to soup. Season with 1 teaspoon soy sauce and umeboshi vinegar to taste. Simmer 5 minutes more. Serve and garnish with chopped scallions.

Note: You may add the corn cobs at the start of cooking to add flavor, and remove them before adding the vegetables.

Onion Soup

Ingredients:

4 medium onions, cut into crescent moons
Sesame oil, plain or toasted
5-6 cups water
1 piece of kombu, no larger than a postage stamp, soaked 45 minutes and cut fine (toss soaking water)
3 dried shitake mushrooms, soaked 1 hour, and cut fine (save soaking water)
Sea salt
Scallions, chopped
Sweet rice miso, optional
Plain mochi, optional

Preparation:

Sauté onions in sesame oil until caramelized. Add a pinch of sea salt while cooking to bring out sweetness of onion. Add all other ingredients (except for miso and mochi) to pot, including shitake soaking water. Bring to a boil, then simmer for 20-30 minutes. You may season with sea salt or sweet rice miso. If using miso use a ½ – 1 teaspoon per cup of water. When serving grate mochi on top and garnish with chopped scallions.

Navy Bean Soup*

Ingredients:

1 cup navy beans
1 onion, diced
½ cup fresh sweet corn
¼ cup celery, diced
4-5 cups water
¼-½ teaspoon sea salt

Preparation:

Wash navy beans. Place beans and water in a pot. Bring to a boil. Reduce flame to low and simmer about 45 minutes. Add onion, corn, celery, and sea salt. Cover and simmer another 20 minutes or until beans are very soft. Garnish and serve.

Beans

Tips for Cooking Beans:

- Soak dry beans for several hours or overnight before cooking them. With the exception of aduki beans, never use the soaking water to cook them in. Drain the soaked beans and use fresh water.
- Note that aduki beans are sold under different names. You may find them with the name "aduki," "azuki," or "adzuki." They are all suitable for use.
- You can use kombu seaweed in beans if you like. A small piece of helps to break down protein, cause less gas, and add minerals to your meal. Because seaweed is so salty, we have to be careful not to use too much. Only use a piece the size of a postage stamp, soak it for at least an hour, toss the soaking water, and add the kombu to the beans when you begin cooking them.
- Remember not to season the beans until they are soft. If you add salt or soy sauce too early, they'll never soften up.

Aduki and Sweet Rice Patties

Ingredients:
1 cup sweet brown rice
¼ cup aduki beans, soaked for several hours or overnight
2 ½ cups water
Sesame oil

Preparation:
Drain the soaked beans and place in a pan with the sweet brown rice and water. Bring to a boil, cover, and lower heat to a simmer. When the water

is completely absorbed, usually in about 45 minutes to an hour, it is ready. Set aside and let cool. When cool enough to handle, form into patties. Heat the sesame oil in a frying pan, making sure you have it about an eighth to a quarter inch deep. When the oil is hot, place patties in the pan. If there is no sizzle, the oil isn't hot enough and the patties will become too oily. You can test the oil with a small amount of rice first. Fry several minutes and let the first side get crispy before gently flipping over and frying the other side. Remove from the oil and place on a few layers of paper towels to absorb excess oil. Serve with Brown Gravy (recipe below).

- *Sweet brown rice is stickier than plain brown rice, so it holds together well to form patties.*

Brown Gravy

Ingredients:
2 cups water or vegetable broth
1 tsp sesame oil
1 onion, diced
2 cups mushrooms, diced
2 tablespoons whole wheat pastry flour or kuzu
Soy sauce

Preparation:
Gently heat sesame oil in a pan and sauté the onion and mushrooms. Dust with flour and mix to coat the vegetables. Slowly add water, let it come to a simmer, and keep stirring. Then add soy sauce to taste and simmer 5 minutes more.

- *If you don't want to use flour, you can use kuzu instead, but be sure to dissolve it in a small amount of cold water before adding it to the gravy.*

Aduki Beans and Squash

Ingredients:
1 cup aduki beans, washed and soaked several hours or overnight
1 cup or more buttercup squash or Hokkaido pumpkin, seeds removed and cubed—leave the skin on (this is why we use organic squash)
¼ teaspoon sea salt
A piece of kombu, no larger than a postage stamp, rinsed and soaked 1 hour
Water
2 tablespoons barley malt, optional

Preparation:
Place the kombu, beans, and squash in a pot. Gently add water to cover the squash. Bring to a boil, reduce flame to low, cover and simmer for about 2 hours. Check regularly to see if more water is needed. In the last 30 minutes, add sea salt. You may add barley malt now if using.

Baked Navy Beans

Ingredients:
2 cups navy beans, soaked overnight
2 medium onions, quartered
Water
½-1 teaspoon sea salt
2 tablespoons barley malt

Preparation:
In a ceramic bean pot with a lid, place beans and onions with enough water to cover by an inch. Bake at 350° for 2½ – 3 hours, checking periodically to make sure they are not drying out. If so, add some more water. When beans are soft, add ½-1 teaspoon sea salt and 2 tablespoons barley malt. Bake 20 minutes more.

Three Bean Salad

Ingredients:
1 cup cooked kidney beans
½ cup cooked chickpeas
2 cups green beans
½ cup onions, cut small

Preparation:
Bring water to a boil and quickly blanch the green beans and onions. Mix them into the cooked beans. Toss with one of the dressings below and serve.

Umeboshi-Parsley Dressing

Ingredients:
½ teaspoon sesame oil
1 umeboshi plum
¼ cup umeboshi vinegar
½ cup water
1 teaspoon parsley, cut fine
1 scallion, cut thinly on a diagonal
¼ cup cucumber, cut thin

Preparation:
First, heat the sesame oil gently and let cool. In the meantime mix the other liquid ingredients together, as well as the umeboshi plum (remove the pit). Then add the vegetables. Add the sesame oil and gently mix together and let stand 20 minutes.

Shoyu-Parsley Dressing

Ingredients:
1 tablespoon olive oil
½ teaspoon shoyu soy sauce

¼ cup brown rice vinegar
1 tablespoon grated onion
1 tablespoon parsley, finely cut

Preparation:
First, gently heat the oil and let cool. Mix with the other ingredients and let stand 20 minutes. You may add water to dilute if desired.

Chickpea Stew

Ingredients:
1 cup chickpeas, soaked several hours
1" piece of kombu, soaked 1 hour (toss soaking water)
2 onions, cut large
2 carrots, cut large
1 cup string beans
¼ cup tahini
1 umeboshi plum
1/3 cup cooked millet, optional
Shoyu soy sauce, optional

Preparation:
Place the soaked kombu in the bottom of a pot; it should be the size of a postage stamp. On top layer the onions and carrots. Next place the chickpeas on top of the vegetables, and finally the millet (if using). Add water to cover the beans, bring to a boil, then simmer for about 40 minutes, or until beans are almost done. Be sure to add water if needed to prevent them from drying out. In the last 10 minutes of cooking, add the string beans. Purée the umeboshi plum into the tahini in a suribachi, removing the pit. You may add shoyu soy sauce to taste if desired. Add this mixture to your stew.

Carol Louro

Pinto Beans*

Ingredients:
2 cups pinto beans, washed and soaked several hours
1 onion, diced
½ cup carrot, diced or quartered
Water
¼-½ teaspoon sea salt per cup of beans

Preparation:
Place soaked beans and vegetables in a pot. For each cup of beans add 3 ½-4 cups water. Bring to a boil, reduce flame to low, cover and simmer until about 80% done. Then add about ¼ teaspoon sea salt per for each cup of beans. The volume of salt may be less if you are making a large quantity. Continue cooking until beans are soft. Remove cover, turn flame to medium, boil off excess liquid, and serve.

Red Lentils*

Ingredients:
2 cups red lentils, washed
1 onion, diced
Water to just cover (4-5 cups)
¼-½ teaspoon sea salt per cup of beans

Preparation:
Place lentils and onions in a pot. Add enough water to just over them. Bring to a boil, reduce flame to low, cover and simmer until about 80% done. Then add about ¼ teaspoon sea salt per for each cup of beans. The volume of salt may be less if you are making a large quantity. Continue cooking until beans are soft. Remove cover, turn flame to medium, boil off excess liquid, and serve.

Aduki Beans with Apples and Raisins*

Ingredients:
2 cups aduki beans, washed
1 cup dried apples, soaked and quartered
1 cup raisins, soaked
Raisin and apple soaking water
Additional water if needed
¼-½ teaspoon sea salt per cup of beans

Preparation:
Place beans, apples and raisins in a pot. Add soaking water, plus additional water if needed to equal 6-8 cups. Bring to a boil, reduce flame to low, cover and simmer until about 80% done. Then add about ¼ teaspoon sea salt per for each cup of beans. The volume of salt may be less if you are making a large quantity. Continue cooking until beans are soft. Remove cover, turn flame to medium, boil off excess liquid, and serve.

VEGETABLES

Parsnips and Onions

Ingredients:
Sesame oil
1-2 tbsp water
3-4 parsnips, thinly sliced into rounds
1 large or 2 small onions, thinly sliced into crescent moons
1 leek, cut small
1/2–¾ tsp rosemary
Pinch of sea salt

Preparation:
Lightly coat a skillet with sesame oil and bring to medium heat. Add the onions and sauté 1-3 minutes. Next, add the sliced parsnips and leeks along with 1-2 tbsp of water. Cover and let simmer 3-5 minutes, stirring once. Add the rosemary and a very light sprinkle of sea salt. Stir to coat vegetables as they cook for less than 1 minute more. Serve hot.

- *Because of the short cooking time in this recipe it is important to slice the vegetables <u>thin</u> so they have time to cook properly.*

Kinpira
This dish is very good for vitality and reducing fatigue. It strengthens our intestines. The word "kinpira" refers to the cooking style of this dish.

Ingredients:
1 cup burdock, sliced into matchsticks
1 cup carrots, sliced into matchsticks

Sesame oil
Water
Soy sauce or sea salt

Preparation:
Brush pan with oil and heat. Add the burdock. Sauté 2-3 minutes. Place the carrots on top. Do not mix. Add water, just enough to half cover the burdock. Cover the pan and simmer 25 minutes. Season lightly with the soy sauce or salt and simmer 5 minutes more.

You may also make this dish using other combinations of veggies, such as:

- *Carrot and Turnip*
- *Carrot and Lotus Root*
- *You may also choose to include the carrot tops or turnip tops in the dish.*

Miso Onions
This is a delicious dish for autumn and winter!

Ingredients:
Onions, whole peeled
Miso, any kind

Preparation:
Cut an "X" into the top of each onion, about a half inch deep. Nestle the onions together in your cooking pot with the "X" pointed up. If you have a clay nabe pot, use it for this dish. On top of each "X" place a small blob of miso, about a half teaspoon. Add a very small amount of water to just cover the bottom of the pot. Cover and simmer about 40 minutes-1 hour, until the onions become sweet, soft, and translucent. Liquid will come out of the onions, which is why you start with such little water in the beginning. Keep an eye on it and add a small amount water if needed so the onions don't burn. Serve 1 onion per person.

Nishime

Ingredients:
Winter Squash, cut into large chunks
Onion, quartered
Cabbage, cut into large chunks

Preparation:
If you have a clay nabe pot, use it for this dish. Layer the vegetables in the pot. Add a very small amount of water to the pot, just covering the bottom. Cover and simmer 40 minutes.

- *If you have leftover nishime, it can make an excellent soup the next day if you add water and 1 fresh vegetable to it.*

Baked Asparagus

Ingredients:
Bunch of Asparagus
Olive oil
Sea salt

Preparation:
Preheat oven to 350°. Trim the bottom ends off the asparagus spears. Coat them in olive oil and sprinkle with sea salt. Bake for 20-30 minutes until tender. When finished, squeeze lemon juice over them if desired.

Boiled Salad*

Ingredients:
1 cup Chinese cabbage, sliced into thin, diagonal strips
½ cup carrot, cut into matchsticks
½ cup daikon, cut into matchsticks
½ cup onion, cut into thin half moons

½ cup celery, cut diagonally very thin
1 bunch watercress or Swiss chard (cut watercress sprigs into thirds, and slice chard diagonally into thin strips)
Water
Pinch of sea salt

Preparation:

Place about an inch of water with a pinch of sea salt in a saucepan and bring to a boil. Boil each vegetable separately in the following order: cabbage, 1 minute; onions, 1 minute; carrots, 1-1½ minutes; daikon, 1 – 1½ minutes; celery, 1 minute; and watercress, 20-30 seconds. All vegetables should be slightly crisp, but not raw. You may use the same water to cook all of the vegetables. After you boil each vegetable, remove it and place in a colander and rinse under cold water until cool. Allow each vegetable to drain and place in a bowl. When all the ingredients have been added to the bowl, mix them together with chopsticks. Add the dressing of your choice and serve.

Waldorf Salad*

Ingredients:

3½ cups shredded cabbage
¼ cup grated carrot
½ cup roasted, chopped walnuts
¼ cup celery, finely sliced diagonally
1 apple, cut into ¼" slices or chunks
¼ raisins

Preparation:

Mix ingredients together in a salad bowl. Add tofu-sesame dressing and mix. Cool before serving.

Tofu-Sesame Dressing*

Ingredients:
½ cake tofu
1 tablespoon grated onion
1 umeboshi plums
½ cup water (you may use 1 cup for a thinner dressing)
½ teaspoon tahini
½ teaspoon lemon juice

Preparation:
Blend onion, umeboshi and tahini in a suribachi. Add tofu and lemon juice. Blend until smooth. Add water and blend again.

Tofu-Mustard Dressing
This is a nice dressing for salads or spread onto a sandwich or with one of the salads above.

Ingredients:
½ pound soft tofu
1 tablespoon freshly squeezed lemon juice
1 tablespoon olive oil, warmed
1 teaspoon prepared mustard
1 tablespoon red onion, minced
1/3 cup dill pickles, minced
½ teaspoon sea salt

Preparation:
Combine tofu, lemon juice, olive oil, and mustard in a food processor until creamy. Add pickles, red onions, and sea salt.

Tempeh, Tofu, and Seitan

Seitan and Mustard

Ingredients:

2 cups of seitan slices
3 onions, cut into thick rings
¼ cup of seitan broth or water
2 tablespoons brown mustard
Scallions or leeks, cut small for garnish

Preparation:

Place the seitan in a skillet with the onion rings on top. Add seitan broth (or water if broth is not available) and mustard. Bring to a boil, cover and simmer for 15-20 minutes. Garnish with scallions.

Sweet and Sour Tempeh

Ingredients:

1 package tempeh, cut into 1" pieces
1 cup apple juice
1 medium onion, cut into rounds
2 carrots, cut diagonally
½ cup whole pea pods
2-3 tablespoons kuzu, diluted in 2-3 tablespoons of cold water
1 tablespoon Brown rice vinegar, or to your taste
Shoyu or tamari soy sauce
Sesame oil
Scallions or chives, cut small for garnish

Preparation
Pan fry the tempeh in sesame oil. Add 1 medium onion, carrots, and some chopped scallions. Add ½ cup water and ½ cup apple juice. Add brown rice vinegar and adjust to your liking. You want just enough brown rice vinegar to flavor and give a slightly sour taste. Simmer for 20 minutes covered. Add whole pea pods, a small amount of soy sauce to taste, and the dilluted kuzu, and simmer 5 minutes more.

- *If you are avoiding fried food, you may skip frying the tempeh, but extend the simmering time from 20 minutes to 45.*
- *Barley malt may be substituted for apple juice. Start with a small amount and adjust to your taste.*

Tofu Salad

Ingredients:
2 blocks firm tofu
½ cup tofu/vegan mayonnaise
1 tablespoon salt or soy sauce to taste

Choose at least 3 of the following veggies:
¼ cup red onion, diced
½ cup celery, diced
½ cup carrots, shredded
¼ cup scallions, sliced
¼ cup parsley, coarsely chopped
½ cup corn, cut from the cob
¼ cup chives, sliced
¼ cup dill, chopped fine

Preparation:
Steam the tofu for 2-3 minutes. Mash tofu and mix the other ingredients with it. This can be served on lettuce or in bread as a sandwich.

Easy Tofu Burgers
Although bread and toast have a tight, hard energy, when you use breadcrumbs with tofu, which has a very soft, relaxing energy, they balance each other.

Ingredients:
1 block firm tofu
½-1 cup sourdough breadcrumbs or ¼ cup cooked millet
¼ cup onions, diced
¼ cup carrot, grated
½ tsp umeboshi plum paste or umeboshi vinegar
Shoyu or tamari soy sauce to taste
Scallions, chopped
Sesame oil

Preparation:
Press a block of tofu between two plates for a few hours to drain liquid. Crumble, and add breadcrumbs or millet. Mix in onions, carrots, scallions, umeboshi plum paste or vinegar, and soy sauce to taste. Form into patties. Heat sesame oil in a frying pan and when hot, place patties in the pan. If there is no sizzle, the oil isn't hot enough and the burgers may become too oily. When crisp, flip and fry the other side. Serve with your favorite burger toppings, or with brown gravy (recipe is found in the bean section).

Scrambled Tofu

Ingredients:
1 package tofu, pressed to remove excess liquid
¼ cup scallions or parsley, finely sliced
1/3 cup carrot, grated
½ cup onions, diced small
¼ cup corn, optional
Sesame oil
Pinch of sea salt
Soy sauce

Preparation:

Sauté onions in sesame oil until translucent. Adding salt to the onion will bring out the sweetness. Crumble tofu and add to pan. Add carrots and corn, if using. Sauté 3-5 minutes more, stirring gently to mix. Season with soy sauce to taste. Turn off heat and add scallions.

Sea Vegetables

Arame with Lotus Root

Note: any of the recipes that call for arame can also be made with hijiki.
Remember that hijiki requires longer cooking time.

Ingredients:
1 cup arame, soaked 15 minutes and cut small (save soaking water)
12 slices of lotus root, cut into thin rounds
Sesame oil
Scallions, chopped
½ onion, cut into crescent moons
½ umeboshi plum, pit removed and cut small
¼ cup water
Shoyu soy sauce to taste

Preparation:
Sauté onions and lotus root in sesame oil. Add arame and cover with water.
Add umeboshi plum. Cover and simmer for 20 minutes. Add scallions and
a very small amount of soy sauce, then simmer 7 minutes more.

Hijiki (or Arame) Salad

Ingredients:
1 cup hijiki, soaked for 15 minutes
1 medium onion, cut how you like
Sesame oil
Corn kernals, cut from 2 ears of corn
½ umeboshi plum, pit removed and cut small
Sea salt
Scallions, chopped

Preparation:
Cut up soaked hijiki. Sauté onion in the sesame oil and sprinkle with a pinch of sea salt. Add the hijiki to the onions with enough water to cover. Cover and simmer for 20 minutes. Add the umeboshi plum and corn, and simmer uncovered for 7 minutes more. Garnish with scallions and serve.

- *Note: if using arame, rinse and soak for about 7 minutes.*

Arame with Onions

Ingredients:
1 cup arame, soaked 15 minutes and cut small (save soaking water)
1 onion, cut into crescent moons or diced. I like crescent moons for the sweeter taste
½ umeboshi plum
Scallions or fresh ginger

Preparation:
Saute onions in sesame oil. Add arame with a ¼ – ½ cup soaking water and ½ umeboshi plum. Cover and simmer 20 minutes. Garnish with scallions or grated fresh ginger when serving.

Nori Cream
This is a delicious condiment to serve with your grains.

Ingredients:
2 sheets nori
¼ cup water
Shoyu soy sauce

Preparation:
If your nori isn't pre-toasted, gently toast it holding it over the heat of your stovetop. Tear the sheets into pieces and place in a pot with the water.

Bring to a boil, then reduce heat, cover, and simmer for 10-15 minutes, mixing occasionally, until the nori is becoming thick. Add just a few drops of shoyu soy sauce, and let simmer another 10 minutes. Let cool and store in the refrigerator.

Macrobiotic Sushi
Sushi and rice balls are good snacks to travel with or take to work.

Ingredients:
Sheets of nori seaweed, toasted
Cooked brown rice, cooled
Umeboshi plum paste

Choose 1-3 of the following filling, finely diced:

- *Carrot*
- *Pickled Daikon*
- *Scallion*
- *Pickled Ginger*
- *Cucumber*

Preparation:
Spread rice flat onto a nori sheet with a wooden paddle. Spread umeboshi paste across the center of the rice. Umeboshi paste helps to keep rice from spoiling, especially if you are travelling. Add any other fillings down the center on top of the umeboshi paste. Roll on a bamboo mat if you have one, pushing and pulling to get it rolled tight, if not just use your hands to roll the nori and fillings into a tight roll. To seal the roll, dampen the edge of the nori with a little water and squeeze the roll in the bamboo mat. Holding the roll vertically, gently tap the roll on the table a couple times to pack the rice down. Cut the roll straight across or at an angle with a sharp knife.

Dipping sauce for sushi
Combine 1 cup water, 1-2 tbsp. soy sauce, 1 tbsp. brown rice vinegar

Carol Louro

Sauteed Dulse and Vegetables*

Ingredients:
1 cup dulse, washed, soaked, and sliced
½ cup carrot, cut into thin rectangles
½ cup daikon, cut into thin rectangles
Sesame oil
Small amount of tamari

Preparation:
Lightly brush skillet with sesame oil. Add daikon and carrots and sauté 5-7 minutes on a medium flame, stirring constantly to avoid burning. Add chopped dulse and several drops of tamari. Cover and reduce flame to low. Simmer 10 minutes or so. Remove cover and cook off any excess liquid. Serve.

Cucumber Dulse Salad

Ingredients:
2 cucumbers, peeled and thinly sliced
2 tablespoons dulse, soaked for 20 minutes and sliced
1 bunch of watercress or parsley, cut small
Juice of 1 lemon
Zest of 1 orange
Umeboshi vinegar to taste

Preparation:
Mix the cucumbers, dulse, and watercress or parsley together. Add lemon juice and umeboshi vinegar and gently mix to coat the vegetables. Add the grated orange peel and serve.

PICKLES

Pressed Salad

Ingredients:
½ head Romaine lettuce, sliced thin
1 cucumber, peeled and cut into thin rounds
½ red onion, diced
4 radishes, cut into rounds
¼ teaspoon sea salt
Brown rice vinegar

Preparation:
Place all ingredients except for salt and vinegar in a large bowl or pickle press. Mix vegetables together, then add the sea salt. Mix the vegetables again, and add the brown rice vinegar to taste. Mix again. If using a bowl, put a plate smaller than the mouth of the bowl on top of the vegetables with a heavy object on top to weigh it down. If using a pickle press, crank to add pressure. Let sit for 20-30 minutes. When liquid has come out of the vegetables, tip the bowl to drain it. The salad is ready to serve.

Pickle Press
By Christin Ritz

Quick Pickled Cucumbers

Ingredients:
2 cucumbers, peeled and seeded
¼ cup red onion, diced small
1 teaspoon sea salt

Preparation:
Add sea salt to cucumbers and onions. Mix together and place in a pickle press. Let stand 45 minutes – 1 hour. Drain water from the press and serve.

Quick Pickled Radishes

Ingredients:
1 bunch red radishes, cut into thin rounds
1 teaspoon sea salt
Brown rice or umeboshi vinegar

Preparation:
Add sea salt to radishes and mix together with your hands. Add a little vinegar to taste. Place in a pickle press and let stand 45 minutes-1 hour. Quickly rinse the radishes and serve.

SPECIAL DRINKS

You should ask a macrobiotic counselor how often to use these medicinal drinks and dishes for your condition.

Sweet Vegetable Drink

This drink is good for relaxing tightness in the body and it has helped me to not crave sweets.

Ingredients:

¼ cup each of winter squash, carrots, onions, and green cabbage, cut as small as you can
4 cups water

Preparation:

Bring water to a boil, then add vegetables. Leave the pot uncovered and bring to a second boil. Cover, lower heat, and simmer for 20 minutes. Use no seasoning at all. When done strain vegetables and drink 1 cup a day. Refrigerate the rest, and make sure you warm it before drinking again, or have at room temperature. Keep up to 3 days, after that discard. Do not use the vegetables in cooking as they have lost their nutritional value.

- *This recipe can be doubled if desired.*

Ume Twig Tea

Ingredients:

Kukicha twig tea
½ umeboshi plum
½ teaspoon shoyu soy sauce

Preparation:
Brew kukicha twig tea. Place ½ umeboshi plum and shoyu in a tea cup. Pour tea into cup and stir. Drink and eat plum when finished.

Kuzu Tea

Ingredients:
1 teaspoon kuzu powder
Water
Sea salt or shoyu soy sauce

Preparation:
Dissolve 1 teaspoon kuzu into cold water. Add 1 cup of boiling water and stir well. Add a pinch of sea salt or a few drops of shoyu.

Ame Kuzu Tea

This is a very relaxing drink. If desired, the apple juice can be omitted in favor of just water.

Ingredients:
1 teaspoon kuzu powder
Cold water
½ cup apple juice or cider
1-2 teaspoons brown rice syrup or barley malt, optional

Preparation:
Dissolve kuzu into 1-2 tablespoons cold water. Add another cup of cold water to the dissolved kuzu. Add brown rice syrup or barley malt if using, and apple juice. Bring to a boil stirring constantly. Reduce heat to very low and continue stirring until translucent. Drink hot.

Black Soybean Tea

Ingredients:
1 cup black soybeans
4 cups water
2 teaspoons brown rice syrup, optional

Preparation:
Place black soybeans and water in a pot. Bring to a boil. Lower heat and simmer for 30-45 minutes. Strain the beans from the liquid. Add brown rice syrup to liquid if using. Stir to dissolve, and drink while hot.

- *Beans may be reserved and cooked further to incorporate into a bean dish.*

Granny Smith Apple Drink

Ingredients:
1 granny smith apple

Preparation:
Grate the apple. Using your hands, squeeze the juice from the gratings. Drink the juice.

Carrot and Daikon Drink

Ingredients:
½ cup grated carrot
½ cup grated daikon radish
2 cups water
½ umeboshi plum
Shoyu soy sauce

Preparation:

Bring water to a boil with carrots and daikon gratings. Add ½ umeboshi plum and simmer 3 minutes. Add a few drops of shoyu soy sauce. Drink broth and eat vegetables.

DESSERTS
Dedicated to Joe Louro

This section is dedicated to my husband, Joe, who loved making desserts. It is my favorite part of a meal next to soup. Years after I started the center, Joe started helping me at cooking class. He really enjoyed the camaraderie of other male cooks like Warren Kramer and Warren Wepman. When Warren and Marquita Wepman came to teach at our center, Joe and I really enjoyed getting to work with another married couple teaching macrobiotics.

Joe Louro

Tips for making macrobiotic desserts:

- Barley malt and brown rice syrup are complex carbohydrates, so they are much better to use than other sweeteners.
- Amasake can also be used as a sweetener. It is made from fermented sweet brown rice and koji.
- Maple syrup can be used occasionally.

When it comes to desserts we also cook according to the seasons. We need to be flexible. If we pay attention to how food affects our thinking and well-being we can make sensible choices and avoid binging. Here are suggestions to make the best seasonal dessert choices:

- Have baked desserts more in winter
- Have pies more in autumn
- Kanten and agar-agar can be used all year, but more in summer. They are good for relaxing the mind.
- Spring fruit include berries, such as cherries, strawberries, and blueberries
- Summer fruits include cantaloupe, watermelon and strawberries.
- Fall fruits include grapes, cranberries, apples, pears and blueberries
- Apples can be used all year
- Winter fruits include pears, currants, and grapes.

Macrobiotic desserts can be an important addition to our diet to help us relax and make balance if we are becoming too yang. Cooked apples with a little brown rice syrup help to ease tension. Apple juice cooked with kuzu is good to help us fall sleep. Hot apple juice helps to relax too, and cooking apple juice with agar-agar is very relaxing and helpful for weight loss. Also, watermelon can be helpful for our kidney health.

Apple Kanten

Ingredients:
1 quart of apple juice
½ cup fresh blueberries, strawberries or peaches, optional
Pinch of sea salt
4 tbsp agar-agar

Preparation:
Place apple juice and sea salt in a pot. Slowly add the agar-agar flakes as you bring to a boil. Then lower the flame and simmer for about 5 minutes. Add berries or peaches (if using). Pour liquid into a bowl and let sit for about 1 hour. That is how long it takes to gel. I like blueberries or peaches best with kanten.

Mocha Pudding

Ingredients:
1 quart pear juice
1 tbsp grain coffee granules or instant organic decaf coffee
½ cup agar agar flakes
1 tbsp tahini
¼ cup rice syrup (optional)

Preparation:
Bring pear juice, grain coffee, agar agar, and rice syrup (if using) to a boil. Then lower heat and simmer 10 minutes. Set aside and let cool. As it cools the agar agar will gel. When firm, add the tahini and blend.

Cooked Pears

Ingredients:
2 pears
1 cup pear juice

½ tablespoon barley malt
Cinnamon, optional
Pinch of sea salt

Preparation:

Cut the pears in half and remove seeds. Place them cut side down in a pan and add enough pear juice to just cover the bottom. Either bake in a pre-heated 350° oven for 20 minutes, or cook on the stovetop on medium heat. After the pears begin to soften, add barley malt, sea salt, and a sprinkle of cinnamon if using.

You may also cook pears on top of the stove in a pan. Cover and simmer them for about 20 minutes.

By Ruby Louro

Fruity Cous Cous

Ingredients:
1 cup cous cous
2¾ cups pear or apple juice
1 cup blueberries, strawberries, or peaches

Preparation:
If using peaches or strawberries, cut them up small. Bring juice to a boil. Lower heat to a simmer, add the cous cous, and cook for 5 minutes. Gently mix the cous cous to fluff and mix in the fruit.

Squash Pudding

Ingredients:
1 medium sweet winter squash, like butternut or buttercup
1 cup water
Pinch sea salt
½ cup barley malt or brown rice syrup
1 tablespoon kuzu
1 cup chopped walnuts or pecans
Cinnamon to taste, optional

Preparation:
Wash squash, remove skin and seeds. Cut into chunks and put in a pot with water and sea salt. Bring to a boil, lower heat and simmer until squash is soft. Pour out the excess water and set aside. Purée the squash. Place back into the pot and add the barley malt and cinnamon, if using. Meanwhile, dilute the kuzu in a few tablespoons of cold water. Slowly add the dissolved kuzu into the reserved liquid from earlier. Add this back to the squash purée, stirring constantly to avoid lumping. Simmer 3-5 minutes. Remove from flame, pour into small dishes, and allow to cool.

Apple or Peach Crisp

Ingredients for Fruit Mixture:
6 medium apples or peaches, washed and diced
1 teaspoon vanilla
½ cup brown rice syrup or barley malt
Pinch of sea salt
¼ cup apple or pear juice

Ingredients for Topping:
1 cup rolled oats
3 tablespoons brown rice syrup or barley malt
Pinch of sea salt
¼ cup walnuts, chopped
½ cup sliced almonds
¼ cup raisins

Preparation:
Preheat oven to 350°. Mix together the ingredients for the fruit mixture and place in a baking dish. Lightly roast the rolled oats in a dry skillet on the stovetop, stirring constantly until golden brown. Place in a mixing bowl. Mix in the brown rice syrup or barley malt, nuts, salt, and raisins. Pour over the fruit mixture in the baking dish. Bake for about 15 mintues.

Strawberry Shortcake*

Ingredients:
2 cups yellow cornmeal
1 cup whole wheat pastry flour
½ teaspoon salt
3 tablespoons sesame oil
1 cup brown rice syrup
½ cup barley malt

1¼ – 1½ cup water
2 quarts fresh strawberries
½ cup arrowroot flour

Preparation:

To prepare the shortcake, combine the cornmeal, pastry flour, and sea salt in a large bowl. Mix in the oil very well. Add a ½ cup of brown rice syrup, the barley malt, and 1 cup of water, and mix together. Put the batter in a lightly oiled cake pan or muffin tin. You should have about 12 muffins. Bake in a preheated 250° oven for 15 minutes. Then raise the heat to 375° and continue to back for another 15-20 minutes.

Meanwhile, prepare the topping. Wash strawberries, remove stems, and cut berries in half. Put the fruit, ¼-½ cup of water, ½ cup brown rice syrup and a pinch of sea salt in a pan. Add the arrowroot flour and mix gently but well. Bring to a boil, reduce heat to low, and simmer until sauce thickens and strawberries are soft. Stir to prevent sticking and lumping. When the cake is done, remove from the oven. Slice it into squares and serve with strawberry topping.

Variation: Instead of strawberries, peaches, blueberries, pears, apple-sauce and other fresh fruits may be used to make fruit sauces.

*Recipes marked with an asterisk were contributed by my friend, Wendy Esko. I would like to thank her for graciously giving me permission to use some of her recipes (or maybe a lot!). They are some of my favorite dishes that we cooked when she would teach at our center. Thank-you, Wendy.

RECOMMENDED READING

Benedict, Dirk
    Confessions of a Kamikaze Cowboy, 2005, Square One

Earle, Stephen
    Awake at the Wheel: Norio Kushi's Highway Adventures and the
    Unmasking of the Phantom Self, 2018, TAT Foundation

Esko, Edward
    One Peaceful Universe: Macrobiotic Cosmology and the Quest for
    Peace, 2017

Esko, Edward and Wendy
    Macrobiotic Cooking for Everybody, 1980, Japan Publications

Esko, Edward and Alex Jack, editors
    Remembering Michio: Collected Essays on Michio Kushi's Life,
    Vision, and Hope for the Future, 2020, IMI Press

Esko, Wendy
    Eat Your Veggies, 1997, One Peaceful World Press
    Introducing Macrobiotic Cooking, 1987, Japan Publications

Gagné, Steve
    The Energetics of Food: Encounters with Your Most Intimate
    Relationship, 2006, Spiral Sciences

Jack, Alex and Sachi Kato
    The One Peaceful World Cookbook, 2017, BenBella Books

Kushi, Aveline with Alex Jack
   Aveline: The Life and Dream of the Woman Behind Macrobiotics Today, 1988 Japan Publications, Inc

Kushi, Aveline and Wendy Esko
   Changing Seasons Macrobiotic Cookbook, 2003, Avery Publishing

Kushi, Michio
   The Macrobiotic Way, 1985, Avery Publishing
   Your Face Never Lies, 1983, Avery Publishing
   Macrobiotic Seminars of Michio Kushi, 1998, One Peaceful World Press

Kushi, Michio and Alex Jack
   The Macrobiotic Path to Total Health, 2003, Ballantine Books

Kushi, Michio and the East West Foundation
   The Macrobiotic Approach to Cancer, 1981, Avery Publishing

Miyaji, Masao and Evelyne
   The ABCs of Vegan Home Cooking, 2014, Blurb

Monte, Tom
   Unexpected Recoveries: Seven Steps to Healing Body, Mind & Soul When Serious Illness Strikes, 2017, Square One

Sattilaro, Anthony J. with Tom Monte
   Recalled by Life, 1982, Avon Books

Sergle, David
   The Natural Way of Zen Shiatsu, 1999, Japan Publications

Stanchich, Lino
Power Eating Program: You Are How You Eat, 1989, Healthy Products, Inc.

Tara, William
Macrobiotics and Human Behavior, 1984, Japan Publications

Wepman, Warren S.
A Man in the Kitchen, 2000, One Peaceful World Press

Zumdick, Bettina
Authentic Foods, 2012, CreateSpace
Dreams and Uncharted Dimensions of the Soul, 2018, CreateSpace

Made in the USA
Middletown, DE
14 August 2020